Frol...
Chinos
to
Kilos

STEVIE
BATES

BASHER
PUBLISHING

Published in 2021 by Basher Publishing

ISBN Paperback: 978-1-9168885-0-0
Ebook: 978-1-9168885-1-7

A CIP catalogue copy of this book can be found in the British Library.

Author's website: www.stevieschinos.com

Published with the help of indie authors world
www.indieauthorsworld.com

IndieAuthors
World

Acknowledgements

To my dad, Ronald Bates, also a seaman, who was taken from me at the tender and impressionable age of 10 years. I never got the chance to know him!

To my mum, who lived through hell trying to bring up 4 kids alone! I was an extra burden, I ask for your forgiveness?

To my second dad, Ricky McEwan, who taught me all I needed to know. Who protected me through those impressionable years. Who died in my arms when I was 18 years old.

To Jeannie, without her help and commitment, this book would not have been possible.

To Sue, who spent hours on the phone editing.

To Sandy, the mother of my son, whom I have never met! And never will.

To Libby, who reluctantly stood by me while writing this book, detesting my past life.

To all those special people I met, at home and abroad, now long passed away.

To all the prostitutes and sex workers who have the right to make a living however they want. They taught me the wonders of life and lovemaking!.

I thank you all!

Introduction

This story was written from memory, 20 years after the event. It came about when I was sentenced to 3 years in a Moroccan prison. The regime was so strict, there was no work, no food, all you could do was think. I began thinking about all the good times I had had in the past; how lucky I have been, how privileged to have sailed round the world more than 5 times. I have set foot on every continent except Antarctica...(I'm working on that one, it's on my bucket list).

I began drawing the boats that I had worked on, (or should I say, smuggled on) on the cell wall of my space in the crowded prison. There were another 35 men living in a cell measuring 12 x 12 yards. Inmates began asking me about the pictures I drew, some even asked for copies of them. I began recalling every detail of my smuggling activities. I started telling my inmates stories of my accomplishments which they found intriguing. There was even an interpreter relaying my words as most of the prisoners couldn't understand English.

I wrote down my memories on whatever bits of scrap paper I could get my hands on. Many of these were found and taken from me as the regime allowed you none of those items!

All ships, cargoes, places and people I met are from memory, and as true as I can recall. I have changed the names of the main characters to protect them. But many of them have now passed away and this book is a memory to them!

Prologue

At the tender age of only ten years, Stevie suffered the loss of his father. He had been a merchant seaman, but left the sea to marry his mother. He became a miner, and in a freak work-related accident whilst driving a bulldozer underground, the caterpillar tracks entangled with an airline running along the floor causing the dozer to overturn killing him instantly. He was only 31. It made a profound impact on Stevie's future upbringing.

His mother, now a widow, was left to bring up four young children and was finding it more and more difficult to hold down a job. The family moved from Gulley Flats (Egremont), to Parton, a little village on the outskirts of Whitehaven.

With this came a change of school and new acquaintances which brought more trauma for the family. Stevie found himself mixing with several unsavoury characters. It wasn't too long before the troubles started. He started playing truants, clashing with the police, stealing his mother's car and joyriding with several schoolmates, not to mention stealing from his mother's purse.

It was at this point the school board got involved and appointed a social worker to hopefully coax Stevie back on track. However, this was all in vain as Stevie was eventually expelled from school. He then took to running away from home, spending nights in local police stations on several occasions just to get a free bed and breakfast. On one occasion, he managed to find his own accommodation, breaking into a railway hut, Stevie found some detonators that were used for warning train drivers of any upcoming dangers on the tracks. Placing them alongside the track, he then stood on an embankment next to the Tubular railway bridge connecting Anglesey to the Welsh mainland. Throwing large stones to try and detonate them, he was successful, causing thousands pounds of damage to the entrance of the bridge. The line was closed for two weeks!

All this proved too much for Stevie's mother, bringing her to the end of her tether. Finding herself with no choice but to agree to Stevie being sent to a young offender institution, Stevie thought the world had given up on him, or had he simply given up himself? Situated on the Isle of Anglesey, the TRSS Indefatigable training ship was a place where young men could train for a life at sea, would be Stevie's new home. It would be a hard and brutal 15 months, but maybe the kick up the backside Stevie so needed. The establishment was funded by the Merchant Navy, and operated strict Royal Navy discipline. This allowed him not only to finish his basic schooling, but also to learn a wide range of seamanship, skills at which he excelled. For the first time in his life it gave him a purpose, and at the end of his term, Stevie was given a placement on board the '*Marchon Venturer*'. (Or was that just a way for the Government to rid the country of future "would-be-criminals!")...

Chapter One

M.V. Marchon Venturer

It was August 1969 when he joined his first ship the '*Marchon Venturer*', a 2,500 ton bulk carrier registered in Barrow-in-Furness. She was purposely built and contracted out to the mining company where Stevie's father had lost his life. She ran continuously between Whitehaven and Casablanca carrying phosphate, each trip lasting two weeks.

> '*How ironic was that! My first adventure abroad was on a boat from my own town bringing phosphate to Marchon, the mine where I lost my dad! (Well, not quite true.. when I was 12, I cycled through Belgium, Germany, and Austria on a school trip, along with three schoolmates and our headmaster who led us through the journey which lasted a month where we stayed in various youth hostels!)*

Stevie settled into his role on board with ease, although his first 4 days were spent hanging over the side spilling his guts out, suffering from sea-sickness. He was assured by other crew members that it only happens once before you obtain your 'sea legs', their reassurance did not convince Stevie. His position among the crew was deck-hand otherwise known as general 'Dog's Body', always being told to 'get this' or 'go there' or 'clean this' or 'clean that'... and so on!

Once he was told to go and collect fish for their dinner one evening, "Where do I get the fishing rod?" Stevie innocently asked. "You won't need a rod, they're in the bulbous bow" The bosun laughed, "but only the dead ones."

Taking almost an hour to reach below at the bulbous, realising he'd been had, he returned to a raucous laughter from his peers. "Bastards! I'll need to learn quickly!" Stevie swore to himself.

Stevie did not mind, as he was keen to learn although the work was hard and the hours were long, but this never seemed to faze him, the prospects of adventure and travelling the world was way higher on his list of priorities. Being the newest and youngest ('The Greenhorn') on board, he would often be the target of pranks and wind-ups. Like pretty much everything else, he just laughed it off, taking everything in his stride. He was there to learn and have some fun along the way.

On arrival in Casablanca after six days at sea, they were moored alongside a wharf that stretched over a quarter of a mile, filled with boats of all sizes, the Marchon Venturer being one of the smallest. Her two hatches would be opened, above them, two huge conveyor belts were positioned and began pouring Phosphate into the boat at an incredible rate, with an incredible noise to boot.

As expected of the North African Coast, it was pretty hot and very fucking windy. Everything was covered with the brilliant white powder, even their dinners. The glare from the powder due to the sun, was rather uncomfortable on the eyes, making it difficult to keep them open. The whole process took less than six hours, allowing Stevie little time to take in the local sights. He only managed to walk along the pier and the surrounding docks where he encountered several natives selling their wares. You could buy almost anything from bread to 'hashish'. *Well, it was Morocco after all!*. The intensifying heat became unbearable, forcing him to return to the ship without buying any of the local wares.

As they set sail shortly afterwards Stevie stood on deck and watched the flat-topped buildings of the port disappear over the horizon. "I should have bought something', he said to himself, 'I may never be back!" He couldn't have been more wrong. Six hours to load the phosphate, three days to remove it.

The fact that he was just a mere 15 year-old lad, a small fortune in his pocket rather emphasised his restlessness. Basic earnings of £27 per month for a 40 hour week, increasing to 120 hour week at sea gave him a wage of £88 per month.

Returning a second and third time, it was on this trip he began to feel restless, often muttering to himself, "I'm not seeing much of the world aboard this ship."

Although harbouring the thoughts of his restlessness, he did return for a fourth voyage and to say it was to be life changing would be an understatement. This trip was destined to be different, from the minute they docked unusually during the dead of night. They berthed up astern to a huge bulk carrier, making the Marchon Venturer look like a dinky toy moored under her enormous arse end. Across her stern was written 'MV Baron MaClay' and underneath ' Ardrossan' as her port of registration.

"Where is that?" Stevie asked one of her crew members as they worked on the prow deck heaving ropes to tie up. "I've never heard of the place" he exclaimed.

"Somewhere in Scotland", came the answer, "Ayrshire, I believe."

"Really? Sounds foreign to me!" He replied. At that point, Stevie did not have the slightest inkling of just how important a part Ardrossan would play in his life.

The Baron MaClay was huge, with five decks of accommodation situated aft. She had six hatches the size of a basketball pitch. Each hatch was served with an 18 ton grab crane. She was classed as a self-loader/discharger meaning she did not need a port to dock. She could carry, 24,000 tons of cargo, anything except oil. Otherwise known as a 'Deep Sea Tramp' she could go anywhere, with, or without a port.

A party was being held aboard the Scottish giant, and the crew of the Marchon Venturer were all invited. As no work was being done having arrived at night, several of them decided to go including Stevie, even though he was under age, besides the Scots were famous for their drinking. Rather ironic for Stevie having had no previous experience, but who better to teach him than the Scots.

"Never drink anything with whiskey but water," One of the Scottish crew said to him. His name was Ricky McEwan, he was the ship's bosun. He introduced Stevie to whiskey. Having drank the first one, which he enjoyed, he drank some more, leading him to experience his 'first' of many 'first' experiences! A hangover.

Ricky, from Glasgow, spoke like a true Glaswegian. At 38, he looked older. The years at sea had taken its toll on him. He was tall, about 6ft 2in which concealed the weight he possessed, and what remained of his brown hair clung to the sides above his ears, almost covering them, ending with long sideburns at the base of his lower jaw, otherwise clean shaven. His well tanned skin bore weather scars of all shapes. He had a warm smile showing a full set of teeth, although yellowing with his age. He reminded Stevie of his dad!

They joked and laughed all night and were getting on quite well, seemingly on the same level.

I hope he's not gay, Stevie thought, *you do hear it's rife in the Navy.*

Time was getting on, and Stevie was getting drunk, a whole new experience for him. With much work to be done in the morning, and feeling a bit queasy Stevie decided it was time to excuse himself and barely made it to the toilet before emptying the entire contents of his stomach down the pan.

"Are you okay?" Ricky asked. "You look terrible."

"I feel terrible!" He managed to say without sounding pathetic. "I've enjoyed myself but I'd better be going. I hope you don't mind. Thanks for everything, it's been great to meet you. I hope someday we'll meet again."

Out of the blue, Ricky said, "Do you fancy going deep sea?"

"What do you mean?" Stevie asked.

"I mean, sign up here. There's a fellow on board who can't hack it, he's looking for a way back home without jumping ship."

"Is that possible? I mean swapping ships?"

"I can arrange it if you're interested." He got up. "Tell you what, why don't you sleep on it and if you are interested, come on board tomorrow morning and we'll sort it out."

"Okay!" Stevie said. "Goodnight!"

"Goodnight!" Ricky replied.

"Is he gay?" Stevie asked himself again. "I hope not!"

* * *

The next morning Stevie boarded the Scottish Giant.

"Got your discharge book?" Ricky asked.

"Yes," Stevie replied and handed it to him, he showed Stevie to the mess room.

"Wait here, I have to go see the Captain. Help yourself to coffee, I won't be long."

He returned within five minutes and signalled for him to follow. They climbed four decks of plush accommodation and halted outside the skipper's cabin. Ricky knocked.

"Enter!" The cabin was large, consisting of a spacious day room, an en-suite bedroom, a reception and an office, where Ricky and Stevie now stood.

"Stevie is it?" Captain George Towers bellowed in a broad Highland accent. His voice matched his physique, fat to the point of obese. A wild mane of ginger hair with a full beard to match. Deep grey eyes penetrated you as he spoke, occasionally spitting out his words. A true Scot!

"Yes Captain." Came Stevie's reply, slightly cowering in the powerful presence he radiated.

"Bosun tells me you want to go deep sea?" Reaching out for the discharge book and taking it from Ricky, he studied it closely for several minutes.

"I see you're not 16 till next month, that might be a problem. I'll need to speak with your Skipper, what's his name?"

"Captain Ian Leslie, sir."

"Can't say I know him." Turning to Ricky, "Can you arrange a meet?"

"Will do Captain."

Then addressing Stevie, "OK, I'm willing to accept you. But it depends on Captain Leslie. I'll let you know soonest. Dismissed!"

Captain Leslie agreed to the transfer, and Stevie's adventure to the deep seas began. The Baron MaClay set sail the next day. Stevie stood aft once more, watching the skyline of Casablanca disappear again from view. This time, instead of six days to Whitehaven, it was now six weeks to Japan!

BARON MACLAY

CALL SIGN GPEIE
21,950 TONS DEADWEIGHT.
13,043 " GROSS
523 X 76 X 32 FEET.
4, 15 TON GRAB DECK CRANES
28 CREW "DEEP SEA TRAMP"
15.5 KNOTS
SCRAPED 2010 PENHIANG.

Chapter Two

M.V. Baron MaClay

It didn't take long to settle in, most of the time was spent exploring. Compared to the Marchon Venturer, the Baron MaClay was huge. Stevie's cabin, situated on the poop deck, was en-suite. It felt like a 5-star hotel. She had a cinema, gym, sauna and games room. She even had a swimming pool on the Bridge Deck. (Not advisable in bad weather).

Stevie's first job was cleaning the bilges. A 3ft square compartment ran the length of her keel used for ballast when she was unladen. (Renowned to be the dirtiest job on board, but somebody's got to do it!)

Armed only with a hard hand brush, a water hose, and all the courage he could muster, Stevie squeezed himself into the tiny gap with great difficulty, and began brushing. The stink of dead fish was so overbearing, he had to crawl back out for fresh air several times. There were hordes of crabs, some dead, but most alive. He was nipped and bitten constantly. Other indescribable sea creatures, sucked in when they took on ballast, hindered his progress. Each one had to be taken out and dumped, that was fine if they were dead. Some of the live ones were a struggle. Finally, after three hours, Ricky arrived.

"Okay Stevie, you can take a break."

No answer!

"Stevie!" Ricky raised his voice. Getting concerned, he was about to get on the radio and call for help when he heard the rustle, clambering, and heavy breathing as Stevie came into view.

Laughing, Ricky bellowed out, "I wish I had my camera!" Coughing and spluttering between laughs.

'I must have looked a sight. My long hair, clamped to my skull, was dripping with sea water. My face was black with seaweed residue. Live crabs were hanging from me in several places. There were several dead water snakes wrapped round my neck, and I was trying to haul a sack full of squid, octopus, and fish of all sizes through the narrow gap behind me.'

"Think it's fucking funny do you? Ha ha fucking ha!" Dragging himself through the exit, he called out, "A fucking hand would suffice!"

Finally, Ricky pulled Stevie out, still chuckling, he asked, "Are you all right? Have you much more to clean?"

"I'll live. I'm almost at the bow, what is the reason for this? There must be an easier way?"

"Cleaning the bilges? They have to be cleaned out each time before taking on ballast again. The only way to do that is cleaned and flushed out by hand. How far are you along did you say?"

"Over three quarters, almost at the bow."

"Get a 20 minute break, when you've finished, that's you done for the day."

"Cheers bosun!" He knew he was the smallest on board. He was the "gofer" after all. And somebody had to do it.

Stevie took everything in his stride. He was so keen to learn, he became a little gullible. Many pranks were played on him. Crossing-the-Line, (The Equator), for the first time was the most traumatising. The old tradition of 'tarred and feathered' was now illegal, (*Thank God!*). Instead, he was stripped, shackled to a bollard, then buckets of iced cold water were thrown at him.

Eight days later, she docked in Cape Town for bunkers, (engine fuel), mail, and exchange of films. The process took 12 hours. She was berthed at least a 2 hour taxi drive from the city, no time for Stevie to explore.

Nine days sail from Cape Town, Stevie was awakened suddenly by alarm bells ringing throughout the vessel. The engine had stalled, and she began pitching and rolling. He checked the time, 0325 hours, jumped from his bunk and went to investigate. He was met by a couple of ABs, (Able Bodied Seaman). Jerry one of them, tall, skinny, with a mop of ginger hair said, "Bosun wants you down below." "What's happened?"

"Looks like the freezers have packed up."

Arriving at the freezers, Stevie was met by Ricky and several Ordinary Seamen, who had formed a chain bringing out boxes of defrosting food.

"Go to the far end and bring out what you can." He told Stevie. "Everything has to be dumped."

Andrew, the plump cook, was trying to salvage what food he could, checking every box and pallet before declaring them unfit. Stevie tugged with all his might on a box of beef wedged in one corner. Suddenly, he fell backwards as the box gave way.

He noticed part of the bulkhead had also given way, frozen to the box of meat. He stared into the hole which confronted him and noticed a shimmering plastic coating. He put his hand through the hole and removed a small package, about the size of a bar of soap. Turning, he saw Ricky entering and called to him holding up the package.

"Bosun, what's this?" Staring at Stevie, Ricky made a gesture to replace the item, and moved thumb and forefinger across his lips, indicating silence. The third officer followed behind. Stevie understood immediately and replaced the box of beef so nothing seemed amiss.

"How long will it take to clear everything?" The third officer asked Ricky. "Couple more hours at the most, sir."

"OK, let me know soonest." He then left.

Ricky looked at Stevie and said abruptly, "My cabin when you finished!" He then followed the third officer out.

Shit what have I done now? I was only following his orders.

It was 4:45pm when Stevie knocked on Ricky's door. "Come in." He entered. The cabin was spacious, a day room, bedroom en-suite, and an office, where they were now. Sitting behind his desk rolling a joint, Ricky took his lighter, lit the joint and took several long drags. Handing it to Stevie, he said, "Let me tell you a story. Do you know what this is?"

Stevie, unsure what to say, took the joint. Ricky went on.

"Have you ever heard of the term '*chino*'?"

"No!"

"A chino is the minimum amount of cannabis you need to make a joint, and that's what you have in your hand."

Stevie took two draws and his head began to buzz. He handed it back to Ricky, who began telling the story. "This is top grade Moroccan Soap Bar. It's made from cannabis. You won't get much better anywhere else. Now you've discovered it, I'll need to cut you in."

Ricky took another draw. "On board, there are a lot of chinos, in fact, there are kilos of this stuff. 7,500 tonnes of them, most of it headed for Mount Maunganui and Osaka. I'm going to put you on the stores crane aft when we reach Japan. All you have to do is keep your mouth shut! Can you do that?"

Through coughs and splutters Stevie said. "You can count on me!"

Three weeks later, and almost out of food, they berthed in Osaka. The process of removing 15,500 tons of phosphate began, (8,000 tons was to be discharged in Mount Maunganui).

A 40 ton refrigerated truck pulled up astern and several workers began loading food on pallets. As ordered, Stevie worked the stores crane and began lifting pallets of frozen food from the rear of the container, dropping them through the stores hatch, where two ABs, Jerry and Tam, were replacing each pallet with Soap Bars. They were then lifted up and dropped onto the quay side where several Japs, (as they were known), placed them inside the truck. The operation which took 2 hours, was well organised.

'Well why not Stevie thought. If you're gonna buy 15,500 tons of phosphate, transport it half way round the world, why not another 7 and a half ton of hash! Yes, well organised! I realized Ricky, Jerry and Tam were the culprits. And now, I am involved.'

That night, Ricky took Jerry, Tam, and Stevie to a hotel he knew. They sat in a private cubicle, and ordered beers from a cute waitress. She gave Stevie a warm smile as she placed down his drink. He smiled back. Like all the female staff, she was dressed in full Geisha outfit. Her jet black hair tied up in a bun and secured with several ornamental clasps. Her silk robe, tight and restrictive, and the Japanese wooden slippers she wore made her hobble. Her pale skin, large oval grey eyes, short stubby nose and plush red lips, all coated with excess make up, made her look like a China doll.

Twenty minutes later, they were joined by two well dressed Japanese men. Ricky got up to greet them with a bow, they returned the gesture. Jerry and Tam also stood up and indicated for Stevie to do likewise. This was all alien to him, but he followed protocol. They sat down and the same warm smiling waitress took their order of sakě. He didn't know Ricky was fluent in Japanese and was fascinated listening to the debate they were having. After about 15 minutes, the Japanese rose to leave. Likewise, they all stood up, and after bowing, the Japanese departed.

Stevie sat on the sideline while the others discussed cash, then Ricky handed Stevie a wad of notes.

"That's 75,000 Yen, about £100."

"How much?" Stevie was gob-smacked. "What's that for?" Ricky laughed. "For keeping your mouth shut!"

The night wore on, Stevie was getting a liking for the Japanese warm sakě he was drinking, he was on his third, and was beginning to feel tipsy. "Take it easy with that sakě." Ricky told him, "It's guaranteed to blow your mind or get your money back." He laughed.

"That waitress keeps giving me the eye." Stevie announced. "She's pretty I admit. Oh, by the way, remember you're 18 if asked. They can be fairly strict here with the law. So I'm just warning you, keep your head in check." He indicated to Jerry and Tam saying, "OK gang, drink up and we'll go."

"Go where," Stevie asked as the waitress, passing, blew him another kiss. "Can we not stay here?"

"Trust me!" He said, "I'm taking you to a special place."

They left with the waitress looking regretful. After a 10 minute walk they passed through a door, down a spiral staircase, and entered a low lit lounge bar. It was quite full. They were directed to an empty cubical at the far end by two beautiful Geisha girls.

"I think I'll just have a coffee." Said Stevie. The walk in the fresh air had gone to his head, and all he really wanted was to sleep. "You OK?" Tam asked, "looks like a whitey coming on."

"Just feel a bit shitty. I'll be fine after a couple of coffees." And he was! Later, Stevie was taken upstairs by three beautiful Japanese Geishas, they treated him like a God. They fed him. Stripped and bathed him. Towel dried and donned him in a luxurious silk robe. They removed their outfits leaving them naked. They led him to a huge circular bed and began caressing, kissing, and licking his whole body. One of them sat on her shins and placed his head between her upper thighs, her long hair caressing his chest each time she planted her lips on his. Her tongue penetrating every crook and crevice of his inner mouth. Occasionally, releasing her tongue from his mouth and ramming it in his ears. She twerked his nipples between fore finger and thumb, making them painfully ridged, while the other two gave him a double blow job. From then on, several hours passed while they almost screwed him to death. Eventually, succumbed to exhaustion, he feel asleep. The experience was so overwhelming, it took Stevie several days to recover. Walking around in a trance most of the time, his poor prick suffering numbness and fatigue. He was only 16 when these three hookers, who were nearly twice his age, took his virginity!

* * *

Back onboard, within minutes of discharging the required amount of phosphate, two tugs, were already tying up to haul the ship away from the quayside. Immediately out of the Harbour Basing, the Pilot disembarked, and both engines were ignited. The continuing engine noise gave those on board the feeling of normality. All shoreside activities forgotten. After dinner that evening, the Captain ordered a meeting for all hands in the mess-deck.

"We've been alerted that Typhoon Ida is approaching. She is two days away but picking up speed. We will be heading due South, and hopefully clear Cape Sata before dawn, which should give us some shelter. Be aware men, we have a rough voyage ahead of us. That is all. Dismissed."

At 5am, the ship cleared Cape Sata, the most southerly point on Japan's Southern Island. Ida was moving faster than predicted, and was almost upon us, when the Captain ordered to `heave-to` and headed into the same direction as the storm. As Ida's forward winds engulfed the ship, the noise was deafening, she began pitching and tossing as mountainous waves crashed over her stern, pushing the ship forward. Then, after an hour or so, the wind abated, the waves began to settle, and the sea became like glass. They were in the eye of the storm, heading along with six other ships all seeking calmer waters. The respite was temporary as the second bout of strong winds caught up. The swell increased once more as the rear of Ida passed over us, thrashing at the poop deck astern. An hour or so later, the ship reached calmer waters but within minutes, a loud noise from two Chinese MIG Fighters appeared in the skies above. They circled all six ships for several minutes, before disappearing as fast as they arrived.

Later, in Stevie's cabin, he asked Ricky if he knew what the Fighters were about.

"By the time the storm passed us," He said, "we were in Red China waters, apparently, foreign ships must display their National Flags."

"Did we?"

"No! And I'm surprised the skipper hadn't issued orders beforehand, he should have known. They were ready to shoot us out of the water."

"We were lucky they didn't then."

Thoughts were now on the three-week voyage South to New Zealand. All crew members settled for the three weeks of working as much as possible to accumulate funds for the next port of call. The well-stocked bar on board, if anyone fancied a drink was empty more times than it was full, but time passes quickly, and before you realised it, you were docking.

Mount Maunganui was a small fishing village situated on the Northern Isle of New Zealand about 250 miles south east of Auckland. It was named after a huge volcano situated at the end of the long sandy beach which stretched for over 165 miles. A narrow passage between the mountain and the harbour, was the only access, making it prone to neap tides.

Thanks to Typhoon Ida, the ship arrived two days late and missed the tide, so was unable to dock. Although most of her cargo was discharged in Osaka, there was still 8,000 tons on board. Once again, we sat at anchor offshore, waiting for the next available high tide, which was due in three days.

Not long after the engines stopped, Stevie was sitting in a beach chair, with his heaving line, wire trace, customised meat hook, bait, and other little gems like weed, and munchies ready to spend the night fishing! He fixed a large lump of liver the cook gave him to the hook, secured the line to the end one of the aft winches and threw the other end overboard. He sat back, prepared for a long night. He'd been told that sharks hunt at night, so he waited and waited till it had become quite dark. Hours passed, the only movement was car lights moving along the shore-side, the sea shining like glass in the moonlight.

He saw nothing but a small water snake. Eventually, sleep was getting the better of him, so, after a couple of joints, he decided to call it a night. At anchor, not much work gets done. Only a skeleton crew are needed for the watch, so he could have a long lie in.

He was awakened after several hours by Tony, the 3rd engineer.

"Stevie. Get up. You'll need to come and see this."

Half awake, he scrambled from his bunk.

"What is it?"

"I hear you were fishing last night. Catch anything?"

"You trying to take the piss?"

He laughed. "No. But someone else is!"

Stevie was not a pleasant person first thing in the morning, he was getting very agitated, "Tony, what the fu..."

"Come on, you've got to see this!"

Following him onto the Poop deck, rubbing his eyes, Stevie could not believe the vision that confronted him. He counted three different shark species. There were two Hammerheads, a White Tipped Shark, and six Bull Sharks. Stevie stood in shock, as two ABs, Basher and Joe hauled another in over the side. Talk about pissed-off! All night Stevie had spent watching and waiting, and for what? Absolutely fuck all! Now everyone was in the act.

Apparently, the galley boy had dumped slops over the side first thing that morning and noticed a flurry of shark action. It became a free-for-all. All the guys had to do was use grappling hooks, reach over the side, stab the nearest one, then heave it on deck.

Yeah! Stevie was really pissed off. Once fully alert, he joined the melee, but the school were moving away following a shoal of herring. Davy appeared on the scene laughing.

"Right fellows, better get this lot cleaned up before I get shit from the Skipper."

"I was in my bed." Stevie said. "I have nothing to do with this!"

Basher and Joe began cutting off fins, removing their jaws, photographing them, and then throwing them back overboard. They were soon gobbled up by their friends.

* * *

Stevie was determined to catch a shark. To him, it was like winning your first Grand Prix so as he had to get the `Monkey` off his back, he decided to try again that night. He gathered his fishing gear together, cluster light, to attract them, heaving line secured to aft winch, meat hook with bait secured, a bucket of slops, bit of grass, a bottle of The Famous Grouse, and his beach chair. Tossing the slops over the side, he sat down, and skinned up. And waited. He drank a whiskey and waited, drank another, and waited some more. Occasionally, one of the crew would join him, have a wee dram, then wish him good luck etc. He sensed the crew were secretly laughing at him. And still he waited!

Around 4:30 am, Stevie was about to give up, when suddenly, he felt a tug on the line as it began reeling out, gathering speed. He ran over to the winch, switched it on and locked it, then back to the guard rail. It was just before dawn, the blackest of night, or so he'd heard and even though there was the cluster light, the line had run out some way, so he couldn't see much in the darkness.

Whatever was tugging the line? Stevie, filled with anticipation rushed back to the winch, and set it to haul in. Back at the guardrail, grasping the line with both hands, he waited for the slack to be taken up and the winch took the strain and began hauling in. It took several minutes before he caught a glimpse of what had taken the liver. Stevie naturally assumed it was a shark, like the ones that were landed yesterday. As it got closer, he took a different view. Whatever it was, shark or otherwise it was huge.

As it began to reach the surface, thrashing around madly, Stevie realized as there was no way he could land this monster, he called for help!

He gasped with excitement, suddenly realizing it was a Blue Shark.

"Help!" He shouted over and over again hoping someone was awake. He knew the first watch had changed, and Harry the 3rd Officer would be on duty.

Stevie, now was getting frantic, raised his voice. "HELP!"

There was no way he was letting this monster get away. It was by far the biggest shark he'd seen. The strain on the winch had come to a crawl, struggling to haul in and was almost at snapping point.

Harry arrived grappling hook in hand and began stabbing at the flesh. Stevie did the same, but to no avail. By now, the shark was at deck level, banging and thrashing around, frantically, trying to break free.

Thankfully, Basher and Ian arrived bearing hooks and they got a firm hold. There was no way they could have landed the beast without them.

"After three." Said Harry. "1. 2. 3. Heave!"

It took almost a half an hour to land the monster. During the process, Stevie's lower leg rubbed against its skin and the result looked like an elephant gun wound. Blood was seeping from several gashes.

"Wow!" Said Basher. "Definitely the biggest Blue Shark I've seen!"

"I'd better get back to the bridge." Said Harry. Then turning to me he added, "and you better get the steward to look at your leg!"

Once the shark had stopped thrashing around, Stevie feeling so elated, began prodding it to make sure the beast was dead. Ian, one of the ABs secured a rope around its tail and hoisted up on the stores jib. 14ft. 7ins. she measured. We had no way of establishing her weight, but her head span measured 5ft 5ins. across. She sure was a monster! We made an estimated guess of weighing in at over 450 kilos.

Basher had his camera and took several photos before she was let down. I was given the task of removing her jaw and fins to claim my prize. However, no matter how much I tried I couldn't do it. I was absolutely knackered! Basher took the knife and did the honours for me. Once completed, it took the four of us to throw her overboard.

Then it was time for bed!

When we finally docked alongside, I was invited ashore with Davy, Basher, Ian and Willie, to the nearest bar. It was sparse, with a dusty floor, little light and a slight smell of annabis. A half dozen tables lay in a mishmash with no particular order. We sat at one big enough to accommodate all of us and a waiter approached to take our order. As I was underage, I drank coffee while the others had beer. There were a few locals mingling around, and one in particular overheard our accents.

"Where you guys from?" He asked

"Scotland," said Davy.

"Ah yes. Scotland. You're off the boat then?"

Some of the others came forward, and as the night wore on, we became quite popular. The locals kept offering us more beer. I refused more coffee and began bragging about the Blue Shark I'd caught that morning.

"A Blue Shark?" One piped up. "You must be mistaken, there hasn't been a sighting here for over two decades."

"I have photos." I answered.

Another local, standing down the bar from where we were, came over and introduced himself.

"Hi, my name is Aubrey, and I work for the local newspaper. I'm very interested in your story. If what you say is true, I'd like to see your photos?"

"Tomorrow's fine with me if you want to come aboard?" I said.

Aubrey arrived the next morning with a photographer.

"You won't get any photos of the shark now. It was thrown overboard." I explained. "I only have its dorsal fin and jaws."

"That's OK, you'll be on the front-page tomorrow." He said. "How does that feel?"

I felt a little excited. I've never had a 'claim-to-fame' before.

Sure enough, the next morning there I was, proudly standing next to my catch souvenirs. The local Radio Station SA545 also got involved and I was interviewed and even mentioned on the New Zealand national news. The headline announced. `The Return of Blue Sharks to New Zealand' with a short story about the teenage Scotsman making the catch. I became a celebrity!

I felt sad leaving Mount. Maunganui. I enjoyed myself a lot. But also, I felt proud. Not only had I caught my first Shark, a Blue one at that but I'd earned my first `Claim–to–Fame'.

Our next Port of call was Hobart, Tasmania, to load 15,000 tons of wheat for Lumut.

"Where's that?" Stevie asked Ricky whilst stowing away mooring ropes that were not needed.

"In the Manjung District, Malaya. It's my third visit."

"Any contacts?"

"There was, but I'm not sure now."

"How much is left? Asked Stevie. "I thought we discharged it all in Osaka?"

"Do you think I wouldn't keep some for personal use? What have you been smoking the past months?"

'I'd often wondered why he would occasionally give me a 'quarter'. He did make sure I was stoned every night, so I always slept well. Was that the 'dope'? He would insist we went ashore stoned, but I didn't go ashore in Hobart. I took the time to correspond with my family. Most crew members wrote in the evening, but was usually stoned, so didn't bother'.

Eighteen hours loading grain in Hobart, then, a ten-day voyage to Lumut. Arriving at Pangkor Island, the pilot boarded and guided the ship along the snaking Penang River. Jungle covered both sides of the river and Stevie counted eleven Asian Alligators lying along the banks. After seven hours of steaming and finally clearing a headland, the ship was met by two tugs, that skilfully manoeuvred the vessel towards a small jetty supported on stilts, rising out of the murky waters that emerged from the jungle. Hordes of dockers swarmed and before the ship was securely moored, trucks had appeared ready for the grain. The ship's 18-ton grab cranes were used to unload the cargo.

Stevie spotted more alligators within yards and several small boats, tied to the jetty, some displaying their wares, while others were boat taxis. Lumut lay on the opposite bank. Once more, many of the buildings were on stilts. Some showed the signs of age, decaying and unsafe, their supports rotting away in the river but several new buildings stood above the trees, indicating the town centre.

'That's the reason for boat taxis, to take you to town. Fuck falling overboard here, you'd be eaten alive in five minutes. The scheduled time for unloading was 4 days'.

Each taxi held ten persons. Stevie sat amidships, where he felt safer. The crossing took twelve minutes, and as soon as it docked, he scrambled to get ashore before being overwhelmed by crowds of natives, eager for greetings, wanting to shake everyone by the hand, or simply touch them. Stevie managed to clear the wooden pier as Ricky grabbed his arm. "Follow me."

Passing though narrow winding lanes and dodging stilted buildings, they came to a wooden spiral staircase. A woman, standing in the opened doorway at the top, embraced Ricky tenderly for several seconds, her head reaching Ricky's chest. She was tiny, 4ft.8ins and about 50 years old, but her weather-beaten face made her look 80.

"Your friend?" She said.

"Stevie," Ricky said. "I'd like you to meet a very good friend of mine. This is Maylla."

They too embraced each other.

"Come" She said. Taking our hands, she led us into her home. The strong smell of cannabis mixed with the aroma of cooking was overwhelming. Her house was on stilts and made from wood and bamboo, held together by a strong binding. The furniture consisted of a large table and chairs filling one corner, a large bamboo dresser that took up another corner, a cloth couch and wooden coffee table which filled more of the available space. Other various things hung from walls and ceiling. Stevie's first impression was claustrophobic.

"Sit!" Maylla indicating towards the couch. "Coffee?" Turning her head towards an open doorway she shouted in Malay. Stevie assumed it to be the kitchen as a mouth-watering aroma of cooking emerged from there.

Sitting, Stevie whispered to Ricky. "I thought they spoke English?"

"Most do, but in these rural areas, they speak Malay."

A young woman emerged from the kitchen carrying coffee and cups on a tray. She looked about 20 with beautiful big brown eyes, a pointed nose and full lips. Her long curly black shiny hair hanging over her shoulders, made her look very sensuous even though she wore a plain red and white cotton dress that reached to her feet.

"Hello Ricky," she said in perfect English. "Nice to see you again." She laid the tray on the coffee table, Ricky stood, and they embraced one another, kissing cheeks.

"And who is this handsome fellow?"

Stevie stood and outstretched his hand. "Stevie" he said, "and you?"

"Raquela." Her smile was warm and inviting as they shook hands. "Pleased to meet you."

"Likewise. Your eyes are beautiful."

"Thank you."

"Behave yourself Stevie," Ricky said, "She's married with two children."

"Really? She doesn't look old enough."

They laughed and Ricky sniggered. "How old do you think she is Stevie?"

"20, 25, maximum."

Raquela blushed and giggled.

"She's 42." Ricky said. "She could be your mother!"

He was stunned. She was an amazingly attractive woman, whoever her husband was, he was a very lucky man. Stevie felt so envious.

Maylla and Ricky left through another door. Raquela, asked Stevie if he was hungry. Although he had not long eaten his dinner, he didn't want to seem impolite, so said he was. "Here, try this!" She said handing him a lit joint. He took two draws and his head began spinning. Maylla and Ricky returned embracing one another and laughing. She kissed his cheek and entered the kitchen.

"Try this." Stevie handed Ricky the joint.

"Where did you get that?" He asked, coughing. "It's good shit!"

Freshly cooked food arrived. A large cooking pot was first placed in the centre of the table, followed by four bowls, a plate of bread, and a jug of water.

"What is it?" Stevie whispered to Ricky.

"Boiled chicken and rice." Interrupted Raquela.

Ricky laughed. "She has acute hearing." Stevie's face reddened.

Once the meal was over and the large pot was empty, Ricky began thanking Maylla for the meal, and gestured for Stevie to do the same. Goodbyes were exchanged and they left.

Stevie followed Ricky between stilted houses and stores, until he climbed another spiral staircase. Reaching the top, they turned and walked along a stilted bamboo walkway.

Stevie hesitated, "Is this safe Ricky?"

"Sure, come on," he began jumping, causing the walkway to swing and bounce about. Stevie hung on like grim death.

"Pack it in." His face was a picture of horror.

Ricky laughed. "It's safe Stevie, trust me!"

Slowly and tenderly, Stevie moved forward, gaining confidence with every step, following Ricky as he curved, and snaked between house landings, until they arrived at an open doorway. Loud music echoed throughout the area.

Entering, the smell of cannabis was overpowering. They were met by three young girls who took their jackets and led them to a large sofa.

One in particular caught Stevie's eye. She looked 18 or 19 years. Her long shiny black hair was tied in a ponytail and reached to her waist. Her slightly slanted brown eyes hypnotised all those who stared into them. Her red shiny lips invited you to kiss them and when she smiled, her brilliant white teeth dazzled you. Like all the other girls, she wore a short black satin maids outfit

"Beer?" She asked, her smile lighting up the whole room.

"Beer for me." Said Ricky, "But my friend is too young, bring him a coke."

The waitress left giggling.

"Thanks Ricky. You're a real pal!"

The bar ran three quarters of the way around the room, large sofas and small tables rested on the bamboo floor. A large bong, a device used for smoking various substances took up table space at each sofa. Customers smoked them at leisure. Most of the sofas were full of people, laughing and generally partying and the couples would leave periodically, disappearing through one of several doors at the far end of the bar.

Although drinking coke, Stevie was stoned. Ricky, and particularly the sexy waitress, continually fed him with joints and as the night wore on, Ricky became a little drunk, and Stevie was beginning to hallucinate.

A waitress, now changed into a long tight pink silk dress, snuggled in beside Stevie. Staring into her eyes, he could make out her lips moving, but couldn't hear her words. Ricky nudged him. He turned to look, but was completely stoned, he couldn't speak.

"Are you OK Stevie? Someone is trying to talk to you."

Stevie turned back to see a pair of beautiful lips mouthing words he couldn't understand.

"What?" He managed to say.

She wrapped her arms around him. "My name is Anju, what's yours?"

Stevie managing to focus his speech, said, "Stevie. I think!"

Anju giggled. "Will you buy me a drink?"

"Sure, but you're the waitress."

"I'm finished working. I know somewhere better than here, my house. I would like to take you there." Her English was good.

"How much?" Stevie managed to stutter.

She clung to his arm, moved in closer and whispered in his ear. "Later, you can give me what I'm worth." She helped Stevie to his feet and led him towards the front door.

"Where are you taking him?" Ricky asked Anju.

"To my home. Not far from here."

"He's my son, he's not used to Malayan smoke, you better look after him." Ricky ordered.

"I promise I will." She produced a note and handed it to Ricky. "My address, you're welcome to call."

Stevie was staggering, having difficulty standing up straight.

Ricky still felt concerned. "How far is your house Anju?"

"Ten minutes from here."

"I think I'll help you get him there. You may struggle alone."

"OK!"

It took the strength of both to manoeuvre Stevie the fifteen minutes it took to reach Anju's home. At one point, Stevie almost fell over the rails on the walkway and landed in the murky waters below.

"You're welcome to stay Ricky." Said Anju.

"No. But I'll be back for him in the morning." With that, he left.

Later, Stevie awoke thinking he was having a wet dream but opening his eyes he found a naked, beautiful woman sitting on top of him, gyrating her pussy around his raging hard cock, lifting herself till Stevie almost fell out of her, then plunging downwards. Realising where he was, he gripped her hips and began moving his hips to match her thrusts. Every time she rose from him, Stevie braced himself for the sensational feeling she gave him as she ground herself down upon him again. She suddenly screamed as the shattering orgasm took over her. She bounced and writhed around like a crazy trapped wild animal, bringing Stevie to an earth moving orgasm, like he'd never felt before. Finally, after several minutes, she collapsed onto him, his cock still inside her and smothered him with kisses, trying to bring herself and Stevie back to reality.

Laying clutching each other, smelling the aroma of sweat and love juice she began kissing and caressing him gently. Moving herself down his love drenched body, Stevie cupped her head, pulling it back so they were level faced and looking at her gorgeous eyes, he said, "Hi! I'm confused, who the fuck are you?"

She laughed. "You don't remember do you?"

Embarrassed, he said simply. "No! But now, when I think about it, you were the waitress who kept feeding me joints."

"I was. Did you enjoy them?"

"I enjoyed you! But I still don't remember how I got here" Looking around, I asked, "Where is here?"

"My home." She kept planting little kisses all over his face. She explained what had happened the night before, how she and Ricky brought him here.

"Your Dad cares for you. He said he would pick you up today."

"My dad?" Stevie smiled to himself.

Back on board that night, Stevie entered Ricky's cabin.

"What was that stuff I was smoking? It looked like red cotton!" Stevie asked. "Fucking blew my mind."

"It's opium based, very powerful. Did Anju look after you?"

"Too much, I woke up with her fucking me!"

Stevie had arranged to meet Anju the following evening at her home. She cooked a meal of smoked trout, salad and baby potatoes. She was a good cook and it tasted wonderful.

They smoked, drank wine, chatted and laughed throughout the evening. Later, they made passionate love all night, till Stevie passed out. When the time came to leave, they hugged each other tightly, her deep passionate kisses overwhelming him.

"Will I see you again?" She asked. Her sexy eyes filled with emotions.

"If I come back, of course you will." He felt tears burning his eyelids. "But that might never be."

Sitting in the taxi boat, waving to Anju standing at the pier, he thought, *she never asked me for money.*

Next port of call was Townsville, Queensland, where they were due to load 22,000 tons of zinc concentrates, bound for Antwerp, Belgium. As soon as the ship was berthed, 4 huge conveyor belts began pouring the black gravel with such ferocity, clouds of black dust filled the air. The noise was deafening! The whole process took 14 hours but there was no time to explore the picturesque seaside town on the famous Australian Gold Coast.

A long seven-week voyage lay ahead, calling only at Cape Town for fuel. The first day at sea was spent washing down the whole ship to rid it of the black gravel. Then ten days to return to the Northern Hemisphere, and 12 days to Antwerp through the notorious Bay of Biscay and the English Channel.

Not berthing in Antwerp until 8pm, once the mooring work had been completed, dinner was served late. During that time, Ricky informed Stevie he was to come to his cabin afterwards.

"Come in!" Came a voice from within when Stevie knocked on the door.

Entering, he was told to sit in front of the desk. Placing two soap bars, and a wad of cash in front of Stevie, Ricky said,

"That should keep you with a smoke for a while. There is also 500 Australian Dollars, about £375. What do you plan to spend it on?"

"I've always fancied a motor bike." Stevie confessed. "May look some up. What about you? Will I see you again?"

"That's possible, we work for the same company."

"Will your family be waiting for your return?"

"I have no family. I spend most of my leave in the pub with friends, I have many of them. This is not goodbye Stevie," this is '*au revoir*', I'm sure we'll meet again!"

They did.....But that's another story!

BARON FORBES

CALL SIGN GYQII
10,681 TONS DEADWEIGHT
12,645 ... GROSS
536 X 72 X 32 FEET.
6. 8TON DECK GRAB CRANES
29 CREW. "DEEP SEA TRAMP"
15.5 KNOTS

SCRAPED 1986
CHITTAGONG.

LIVERPOOL
VICTORIA   VANCOUVER
NEW WESTMINSTER
KANAZAWA
SAN FRANCISCO
NAGOYA   MATSUYAMA
HAMPTON ROADS
SAN JUAN
CARTAGENA
PORT CRISTOBAL   BALBOA
NAKARAMBO
SUVA

Chapter Three

M.V. Baron Forbes

It was Stevie's second week of a 6 week leave earned working 10 month aboard the Baron MaClay.

Staying at his mother's was getting him down. She was strict and set in her ways, often moaning about the state of his room, or not putting his dirty clothes in the laundry, etc. etc. After all, at 17, he was a typical teenager! The long voyages made him grow up very quickly, acting more like a twenty five year old, unlike his ex school friends, who were still immature. Therefore while home, he didn't associate with them. He was a loner!

The cash Ricky gave him was enough to buy a BSA Lighting 650cc motorbike he had dreamed of for years. Dressed in his new outfit of leathers he had bought yesterday, and gathering what cash he had, he headed for the door.

"You look smart." His mother said. "Where are you going?"

"Down town! Been thinking about buying the bike I told you of."

"Must you? They're dangerous." She was concerned, yet I suppose every mother would. "Better to buy a car. Much safer."

"I know, but..."

He was cut off by the phone ringing.

"Hello," answered his mother. "Who? Peter Hamilton? Yes, he's here." She handed the phone over. "I think it's your work," she said.

"Hello." Stevie said with apprehension.

"Stevie, Peter here, sorry to bother you but a job has come up that might interest you!"

"Really? I still have 4 weeks leave?"

"Your leave will be carried forward if you accept."

"OK, what's the job?"

"We need a storeman for the Baron Forbes, she's discharging timber at Queen Victoria Docks in Liverpool, and is due to sail Wednesday." (This was Monday morning).

A storeman, I thought, *that's an excellent promotion. Normally, that would take two or three years.*

He asked. "Why me?"

"Ricky McEwan is signing on as bosun, we don't have a storeman yet, Ricky put your name forward!"

"OK, life's boring at home, you've got me hooked, telegram the details and thank you for the promotion."

"No! I thank you for getting me out of a difficult position."

With that he said goodbye and hung up.

Stevie was elated. "You win Mam, no bike." He handed her his £350 savings saying, "You go and get a car." And ran upstairs to pack.

Arriving as informed, approaching astern of the ship, he noticed black men working on the Poop deck. Odd he thought, and wasn't sure if he was in the right place. Sure enough, written along her stern was "Baron Forbes". And underneath read "Ardrossan".

There was a beehive of activity as dockers worked a 24-hour rota to empty the hatches of timber.

Still unsure, he began walking up the gangway, reaching the top, he was met by Ricky. They shook hands and embraced each other.

"I'm so glad you decided to join, come, I'll show you your cabin."

"Why me? Am I not too young for store-man?"

"The Company were having trouble getting one, and I needed you!"

He checked his watch. "15:20, get yourself settled in. After dinner come to my cabin, I'll fill you in then."

Stevie sniggered, "I've heard that before. Are you gonna tell me another story?"

He laughed. "After dinner!"

His cabin was positioned half way down the port side alleyway. Small, but compact with all amenities. Another door led into a bathroom which he shared with the Cook, Rab, who occupied the adjacent cabin. Once he unpacked, he took a shower, changed, and took a walk-about to familiarise himself with the ship.

But first, he had to find the Captain's cabin. He had an introduction letter addressed to a Captain James McCloud.

Locating it, he knocked.

"Enter."

He looked too young to be a Captain, about 35, tall with dark brown hair cut short and neat. He bore a thin moustache, also neatly trimmed. His big brown eyes behind black glasses were intense and oozed confidence and authority.

Stevie handed over his discharge book, he was told to sit down.

"Stevie Bates eh? Youngest store-man I've had sail under me." He studied Stevie's discharge book for several moments. "I see it's only your second trip deep sea?" It was a question.

"Yes Captain." He began explaining, but Captain McCloud held up his hand

"You don't have to explain, I'm teasing you. I know the circumstances, I just want to know if you're up to it. It's a big responsibility, lots of paper work."

"I'll try my best Sir, I'm keen to learn."

"Good." He stood up and outstretched his hand. "Welcome aboard."

Stevie responded. "Thank you Captain."

He left and continued his exploring.

Much older than the Baron MaClay, the accommodation was less plush. There was a cinema and games room, but no swimming pool. There were two bars, one, up top for officers, and one below for the rest of the crew. Unlike the Baron MaClay which had an all white crew, the Baron Forbes had a black crew; Somalians. Stevie was unsure about that. Not that he was racist, he'd never worked with foreigners before, especially 'Zulus'. (No disrespect.) Made him feel a little uneasy.

The Baron Forbes had 6 hatches served by 6, 18 ton grab cranes. 12 cylinders single prop engine giving her a top speed of 16 knots. Also, unlike the Baron MaClay, she was specially designed to carry timber, the kind that is cut, shaped, then secured with wire strapping.

The ship sailed the following morning bound for Hampton Roads; Virginia, to load 19,000 tons of coal.

'So glad I don't have to clean bilges anymore, I thought, sitting in my new office.(merely a cupboard). Room for a

small desk, a chair, three filing cabinets, and several shelves. Feet up on the desk. This is more like it.

When I thought the world had turned its back on me. Maybe I had turned my back on it! Now, life is going to get much better.'

Hampton Roads, though cold and bleak, was a welcoming sight after a 6 day storm riddled voyage across the North Atlantic. She was unladen making the rolling worse, therefore, very little work was done. For miles around all you could see were slag-heaps of coal. Stevie liked to explore every new destination, but he thought he'd miss this one. Nothing to explore here and was pleased after 12 hours the ship was laden at set sail for Catageña; Colombia.

It was a pleasant surprise to sail beautiful calm seas for the eight day voyage through the Caribbean, Stevie was hoping the engine would fail, so he could hunt for sharks. After catching several already, he wanted to add to his collection, a Caribbean shark would be ideal. But no such luck.

"I thought the coal was going to Japan?" Stevie quizzed Ricky as to why they were heading for Columbia.

"We're here for bunkers. It's a long trip to Japan. We have 10 hours here."

"I see." A taxi arrived. "say again, where are we going?"

"To see an old friend. I hope he's still here."

He was!

"Welcome Ricky." Said a large stocky 40 something, his face covered in a multitude of old scars. They hugged each other for several moments. About the same height as Ricky; 6ft 2in, but stockier. He was bald but wore a huge flamed red moustache almost covering half his face. His huge grin was lost in his moustache.

"Come in, come in." His broken English spoken rapidly. "Take a seat. Beer?"

Stevie sat and wondered whether he had a role in a Spaghetti Western.

Half swinging doors brought them into a dimly lit, sparsely furnished bar. Dusty wooden floors, rickety tables and chairs strewn haphazardly around, on several of them sat unfriendly locals, staring, frowning as they drank from their glasses. South American guitar music blasting from speakers suspended from the wooden ceiling

"Fraydo, this is Stevie." They shook hands.

"You look young and fresh, better watch you around my daughter." Fraydo laughed.

Not wanting to offend, Stevie also laughed, and was almost crushed by Fraydo's powerful hug. From the corner of his eye, Stevie noticed a beautiful señorita heading their way. Guessing about 25 years, she had thick curly red hair, the ringlets covered her shoulders and fell down to her waist. Her large wide green eyes made it difficult to look away. Her small pert nose and lush red shiny lips enhanced her beauty. Her dress, an off-the-shoulder gypsy style with full circle skirt ending below her knees. She carried a tray and towel, Stevie assumed she was a waitress.

She smiled at him as she swooned by, then addressed Fraydo.

"What can I get you Papa?"

'Ha! I thought. Now I understood what he meant by watching me around his daughter, I'd say the same thing if she was my daughter. I began to feel stirrings. Stop it Stevie, she's way out of your league.'

"Ah, Rizitta, you remember Ricky?"

"Nice to see you again." She kissed his cheek. "I hope you're not here to derail my Papa, I'm keeping him on the straight and narrow."

"Now would I do that? Trust me!"

And with the same amount of sarcasm, replied. "Yeah sure." Then averting those gorgeous eyes, she said, "And who's your cute friend?"

"Rizitta." Scorned Fraydo.

"This is Stevie, my apprentice. I'm showing him the ropes."

"Hello Stevie, nice to meet you." She had difficulty pronouncing his name. She leaned forward, shook his hand, and kissed him on his cheek.

Stevie struggled to return the gesture as he'd developed an instant hard-on. He struggled to say anything.

"Are you old enough to drink?

Ricky cut in, "He's 18, no problems."

"Three beers then." She giggled, spun on her heels, and was gone.

Fuck! Did she see that? I feel so embarrassed. Need to get out before she returns. Besides, I don't want to tackle her gorilla Papa.

"Wait here Stevie, Fraydo and I have business." explained Ricky. "We won't be long."

Leaving, Fraydo reminded Stevie to keep clear of Rizitta.

"Shouldn't you tell your daughter to keep away from me?"

His false laugh couldn't hide how serious he was. Rubbing Stevie's hair saying, "Cheeky Monkey. I'm watching you!"

Drowning in his thoughts, Stevie became aware of eyes burning through his scalp. Looking up and around, everyone was staring at him. Stevie felt nervous, scared, and wished Ricky would hurry and return. He felt the warm wetness in his crotch, and walked as fast as he could to reach the loo, and that's another story, the stink almost made him spew up.

Returning to his table after cleaning himself up, trying to hide the stain in his crutch, he was unaware of Rizitta's sudden appearance. Taking his hand, she leaned forward, whispering in his ear. "Come!"

She led him to a back room and took complete control, shoving him into a nearby chair.

"Do you feel more comfortable now?" She purred in his ear. Her beautiful, silky hair falling around him, her aroma bringing him to a very uncomfortable position, his cock now painfully brick hard!

Startled, Stevie jumped up showing his discomfort was still apparent.

She eased back into the seat, and snuggled into him.

Feeling increasingly anxious, and growing in stature, Stevie stammered. "Please Rizitta, your Papa warned me to stay away."

"Shush, relax, he will be away for ages. Besides, I feel responsible for this." She began rubbing his crotch. Suddenly, she stood up, turning round 180 degrees, she lifted her skirt, and sat squarely on his lap. Slowly, she began rocking to and fro with a dry fuck.

By now, Stevie was lost in her actions. Her motions increased speed until he couldn't hold back any more. His balls began to tighten as his orgasm, which begun in his feet, erupted like never before. Bucking and throbbing around bronco style, leaving him in pure ecstasy.

She suddenly stood up. "Feeling better now?" She giggled.

Stevie had never felt anything like that before. He felt exhausted, he could barely move. Somehow, she managed to expose his soaking, raging hard cock, and slowly, eased her beautiful lips down his bell-end, sliding her long tongue around the stem, forcing her mouth to swallow him entirely.

"P l e a s e, no more." He begged.

He'd lost all thoughts of her Papa. Faster and faster she bobbed up and down until another load exploded into her mouth.

Stevie tried desperately to remove her from his now sore and swollen dick until finally, when she'd completely drained him, she released him. Her beautiful bright eyes looked up into his..

"Feel better?" She asked.

Looking at her beauty, he simply said: "You're the best ten minutes I've ever had."

She cleaned and adjusted herself to hide any evidence.

"And you're my best ten minutes too!"

With that she kissed him long and tenderly on his lips.

"Nice to meet you Stevie, I hope we meet again. Goodbye!" And she was gone.

Stevie sat alone, forgetting all the ugly faces around him, contemplating whether that had really happened, he brought himself back to reality. His trousers were still soaking, and struggling to his feet, he began cleaning himself as much as possible.

Stevie just made it back to the lounge bar, when Ricky and Fraydo returned with two large suitcases.

"Everything OK?" Ricky asked. "You look shattered."

"Trust me, you don't want to know." Stevie answered. I was crapping myself, trying to conceal the stain.

"Grab that case and put it in the boot." Ordered Ricky, lifting the other one.

Almost jolting his arm from its socket with the weight, Stevie announced. "What the fuck you got in here? A body?"

"Just do it!" He sounded angry so Stevie complied. With all the strength Rizitta had left him, he managed to place the case in the boot and close it.

Ten minutes later, they arrived at quayside. Stevie was glad that the ship was fully laden, that meant she was low in the water, therefore the gangway was not as steep. He still struggled to get the case aboard. And Ricky eventually had to help. A further ten minutes and they were placed on Ricky's daybed.

Opening them, Ricky said. "This is our latest mission."

Stevie stared at the contents. "What is it? I thought we were moving cannabis?"

Ricky looked at him for a while, then said, "It's top grade uncut cocaine. There are 30 kilos per case, worth £400 per kilo." He pulled a package from his jacket and tossed it to him saying. "Good grass, here, skin up!"

Stevie obliged, but that didn't dampen his fears.

"I know I'm here to learn", Stevie said, "cannabis I can handle, but this, this is a total different ball game, what you're suggesting carries a life sentence., not to mention the Mafia, the Yakuza, drug king..."

"Listen to me Stevie, I'm going to say this only once," Ricky sounded angry, "I have been supplying cannabis to whoever buys it, my job is to ensure that what is boarded, is delivered. From whoever that may be, it's only a customer, but that is not my business, and that shouldn't be yours. The 25 plus years I've been doing this, I've encountered no problems, neither with customs, nor customers. My job, and soon your job, is to deliver the goods, like any business. Fuck the Mafia, or drug kings, if they fuck with me, they don't get their shit. No shit, then there is no sales. No sales, no fucking money. Once the transportation is complete, our responsibility ends."

"I believe you." Stevie had no choice. But an alarm bell rang out, somewhere in the depths of his brain. "How do you get paid?"

"That's your second year apprenticeship." His hearty laugh could fill any room.

I knew cannabis was harmless, But cocaine? I've sailed with Ricky for more than 18 months, he's introduced me to many contacts, but they all dealt with cannabis. Ricky had never spoken of cocaine. What else was I to discover about Ricky?

Thirty-six hours after leaving Columbia, they arrived at The Gatun Locks, Port Cristóbal, just south of Colón, this was Stevie's first trip through the Panama Canal, and the first time he was sailing west.

Stevie was fascinated, watching the ship's mooring ropes being secured to 6 mechanical 'mules'. Two forward, two amidships, and two aft. As soon as the rear lock gates closed, water began rushing in at such a speed, you could see the ship slowly rising, 5 centimetres per second. Within minutes, the forward gates were opened, and the mules began pulling the vessel forward. 5 minutes later, the ships moorings were released and she was free of the lock.

Stevie was undergoing his steering ticket, and given the opportunity to add more hours to his tally.

"How many hours have you done?" Asked the 2nd Officer as he gave instructions to steer 2 degrees to starboard.

"This is my third hour sir."

"Very good! In 15 minutes, we will be arriving at the second lock. Just keep this heading, the Pilot will take over the helm, you stand back, but remain here."

"Yes sir!"

Ten minutes later, clearing the lock gates, I was once more in charge of the helm. This part of the canal was narrower and twisty. known as Las Cumbres. I saw several alligators basking in the heat and sunshine, on both sides, waiting for any unsuspecting victim.

Hope I don't fall overboard; I wouldn't last long.

The second Officer gave continuing headings as the ship navigated the narrow passage. Before long the water widened, passing the aptly named Monkey Island, we approached the third lock.

Once cleared, the engines were kicked up a notch as we entered a huge stretch of water; Gatún Lake, which took 7 hours to cross before arriving at the final lock.

From there, it was plain sailing across the Pacific Ocean to Nagoya, a 26-day voyage.

There were three Officers' wives making the trip. A free World Cruise! One of the perks of being an Officer.

Eleven days at sea, the engine shuddered, coughed, and died. Alarm bells rang throughout the ship as her stability waned and the vessel began rolling.

It was Christmas Eve, two parties had been arranged, one up top for the Officers, the other for the crew, both were in full swing, it was 2200 hours.

Those on duty sprang to their stations, while others not too drunk did what was necessary.

As for Stevie, one too many gin and fresh orange for the first time had him flaked out fully dressed on top of his bunk!

"Stevie. Stevie, get up man!" Harry's voice got louder as he began shaking the half dead body awake. Having no luck with any response, he called out louder;

"Come on Stevie, get up! Help me out man!"

Losing patience, he hauled Stevie from his bunk, propped him up in the shower, and, still fully dressed except for his shoes, turned on the cold shower, and left him.

Returning 30 minutes later, Stevie had managed to open one eye, which was now staring at Harry.

"Look at the fucking state of you," laughed Harry. "Better not let the bosun see you."

Trying to get Stevie up on his feet proved harder than Harry had anticipated, letting him fall back down in the shower cubical just as the cook entered having been awakened by the melee in his bathroom.

"Ah! Rab, wanna give me a hand?"

"Sure. Wow, what a state to be in. Where are you taking him?"

"Just grab his feet, and follow my lead..."

* * * *

Stevie had managed to keep his one eye open, but couldn't recall why he felt so cold suddenly. He reached up to help open his other eye, he found it difficult to focus. Now, with both eyes open, he realised he was wearing only a pair of underpants.

"No wonder its fucking freezing." Stevie muttered through shivering lips as he scoured the area. "Where the fuck am I? And how the fuck did I get here? And what the fuck is that?" Staring into the bright red mouth of a recently caught barracuda, the sharp fangs, blood red throat and green skin left no doubt as to what it was.

Was this a dream I thought? I hope I'll wake up soon, I'm fucking freezing. Never again will I drink gin and fresh orange.

Lifting himself up from what appeared to be a box of frozen meat, was with great difficulty, he realised he was in the freezer room wearing only boxer shorts and flip-flops.

"What the fuck is...?"

The words were difficult for him through quivering lips, he staggered towards the door as the violent shivering began, he had to get out before he froze to death. Using all the strength he could muster, he began releasing the door lock when it suddenly gave way with ease. Stevie fell over the threshold into Harry's arms with both of them landing in a heap on the deck.

On their feet, Rab wrapped a couple of blankets around Stevie, massaging them quickly to get him heated up.

"What the fuck was I doing in there?" were Stevie's first shivering words. "What the fuck happened Harry. I don't remember a fucking thing!"

Harry explained about the shower on the way back to Stevie's cabin, by the time they arrived, the shivering subsided.

"Did you know the engine cut out last night?" Harry said, trying to open the cabin door.

"Really? What happened?"

"Electrical fault in the safety procedures caused the engine to shut down. Took an hour or so to fire up again."

"Did I cause it?"

Harry laughed. "Wasn't that simple".

Still wrapped in blankets, Stevie fell onto his bunk. "How did I end up in the freezer Harry? Tell me!"

"I couldn't wake you at 0600 hours, so I left you in the shower."

"I don't remember!"

"I returned half an hour later, you managed to open one eye, and was muttering about something incoherent."

"I still don't remember."

"I had to tell Ricky who suggested I put you in the freezer."

"Oh shit, am I in trouble, Harry?"

"Well to start with, the Skipper will dock your wages, and as for Ricky..."

"He's angry with me I guess?"

"He told me to put you in bed and you've to take the day off. He'll probably see you tomorrow."

"Is this not Christmas Day?" Stevie asked, finally tucking into his bunk.

"Yeah! And a Merry Christmas to you!" Harry said leaving. "Get some sleep."

Later that day, after an embarrassing dinner, Ricky entered Stevie's cabin.

"Listen Ricky. I'm so sorry..."

"Don't say a word Stevie! I'm so angry with you. I found you in the crews mess, absolutely pissed, blabbering your mouth off, so I had you sent to bed. The Skipper has already said words to me and you better pick up your ideas and get a grip of yourself. I'm trying to teach you many things that I feel you're capable of, but if you're gonna keep acting like this, you won't get far."

Stevie stood with his head bowed, as if being reprimanded by the headmaster at school. Listened intensely to his words he felt so ashamed.

"Forgive me Ricky, I could blame it on the gin and orange, but that's no excuse."

"You're damn right, next time, if it happens again, you're out! Do you understand me Stevie?"

"Yes Ricky. Trust me, it won't happen again. I promise."

"OK! Last chance. Captain has logged you two days wages. Start as normal tomorrow. I'll see you then." And he was gone.

A day late, we arrived at the sprawling city of Nagoya. Like Hampton Roads, all you could see was mountains of coal.

Ricky and I had made up, and after dinner, we took a cab to a place Ricky knew of. Entering a single storey white building, we were met by three huge Japanese men who reminded me of sumo wrestlers. They led us into a large room, scattered with large cushions around low tables. The lights were dim, but you could make out several characters standing around the room as if on guard. A pretty waitress was serving sakě and some sort of crisps with dips.

Ricky left the room to do business, while Stevie sat, shitting himself, afraid to move. The waitress spoke to him, but he couldn't understand. One of the sumo wrestlers approached and simply said. "Eat!" He said, gesturing with his enormously fat fingers. He was offered some food which Stevie accepted reluctantly, not wanting to insult anyone. He felt everyone was watching him. He realised all around him were Japanese Yakuza (Mafia). He prayed for Ricky to return, as he felt himself getting more and more nervous.

Suddenly, Ricky entered, and ushered for them both to leave. Goodbyes said, they were led back outside to an awaiting taxi.

Not one word was said between them till the taxi had travelled several miles.

"Is everything okay Ricky? You're quieter than normal."

"Fucking Japs, they want the stuff for fuck all!"

"Did you get rid of the gear?" Stevie asked.

"Yeah, but they want to pay less each time I come here."

Ricky said no more as we arrived back on board. Stevie was expecting them to hit the town, but sensed Ricky wasn't interested so he didn't bother asking.

Two days later, the ship sailed for Fiji Islands to load half a cargo of sugar, which was bound for Vancouver.

Arriving at Suva, the Island's capital, the ship was too large to dock, so they moored on buoys off shore, and took on 150 dock workers who immediately set up tents on 4 hatches, while the fifth was rigged as their cookhouse. The ship's crew was a mere 28, now you could barely get around. Ricky warned Stevie to keep his cabin locked at all times. He asked Ricky if there were buyers for cocaine in Fiji. "No! But the cannabis is brilliant."

Stevie loaded several pallets of stores. Once completed, and the pilot was aboard, they set sail to Nakarando on the Northern Island; a 5 hour steam.

The scenery was fantastic! A variety of islands covered in palm trees and white sandy beaches, they dropped anchor in the middle of a large lake. Within minutes, long trains of barges filled with 56lbs bags of sugar were being towed towards us from all directions. Ricky put Stevie on No.2 crane. Work began immediately. The hatches were opened to a gap of 3ft. Long metal racks were placed along the gap and dockers stood in a line along the length in exact spaced intervals. Climbing into No.2 cab, he switched on the power. The motor would deafen you, hence he wore headphones. It was hot, so he only wore a pair of shorts and sandals. Stevie manoeuvred the jib above the nearest barge and lowered the hook. Ropes were secured to the hook, and he began reeling in the pallet. Once he'd cleared the main deck, he placed it next to the nearest line of dockers. The closest man would then cut the binds, and began to pass bags of sugar down the line till each man had one. Then taking a knife and slicing the bag, emptying the contents into the hatch. Watching them perform reminded Stevie of an ants' nest. Looks like chaos, but every man worked like clockwork. Our quota was a thousand tons per day.

They were loading 11,000 tons, so he reckoned 11 days to complete. He was glad. If a full load was required, there would be another two weeks at anchor, no way to get ashore.

Every night, after dinner, the dockers gathered up forward, on the Prow. They produced an empty 50 gallon oil drum cleaned and disinfected.

Someone filled the drum with fresh water and another emptied four bags, each weighing 2 kilos of what looked like sand. He became intrigued and watched two or three other men take turns in stirring the powdery mixture for a further ten minutes. A rather large man then stepped forward, Stevie presumed he was one of the gaffers as everyone became quiet and moved aside to let him through. He was handed a sort of clay bowl which he immersed in the sandy coloured liquid. He then downed the contents in one go while everyone else clapped their hands and shouted 'bula'! The bowl was then passed on to the man on his left who repeated the procedure with everyone clapping and shouting 'bula' as he swallowed the liquid.

Without realizing, he had edged myself closer to the gathering and before long the bowl was handed to him.

"No thanks!" I shook my head and tried to pass the bowl along but to no avail.

"Please, you must take some," said a very large Fijian, who refused to take the bowl from Stevie. "It's good, trust me." He had a very broad grin on his plump face.

He couldn't refuse. He stepped forward and dipped the crude bowl into the liquid but only half filling it. He then drank it all as chants of 'bula' sang out. It tasted bland with a grittiness like sand, it wasn't unpleasant and after two bowls, the flavour began to grow on you. In fact, after his third bowl he was almost legless, wearing a '30 bob grin'.

The gathering was now in full swing. A couple of natives had picked up guitars, another brought a tom tom and various percussion instruments, others were singing, some were dancing.

And that was the last he remembered!

The name of the sandy liquid was 'Carva'! It was produced from cannabis grown locally.

Stevie was given two bags when they departed. He had never had such a good time where there were no female company. (Unless you count the three officers' wives on board!)

Once laden, they returned the dockers back to Suva. He watched in amazement. The whole shoreside were full of locals, including females, singing and dancing, and wishing them a safe voyage. He felt humbled, and yet disappointed, his first port without a woman. Prostitute or not!

* * *

The ship made good progress northbound. Her Horton Sulzer 6 RD engine producing 9,600 bhp keeping her a steady 15.5 knots, arriving at Victoria, Vancouver Islands capital, two days earlier than the scheduled 18 days.

"Have you made contact?" Stevie asked Ricky entering his cabin after dinner. "Yes! She's on her way."

"She? You mean you do like women then?" (Although Stevie saw him with hookers, he never spoke of any other females. At first, Stevie thought he was gay! He assumed if Ricky wasn't bent, then he may be slightly buckled. Over the years Stevie met many a gay seaman, and discovered they were only after their own kind). Ricky slapped the top of Stevie's head saying.

"Don't be so fucking smart!"

"Well, come on, who is she?" Stevie was eager to find out.

"Her name is Nora, she and I were school sweethearts, she emigra..."

"Really?! You mean she's Scottish?"

"Are you gonna shut up, or are you gonna listen? He sounded angry. "The only reason why I'm telling you this is because I have to introduce her to you,

she will be your future contact."

Stevie felt like shit. "Forgive me Ricky, this is all new to me. I'm sorry, please go on. I promise I won't interrupt again."

"As I was saying, a year after we left school, her parents emigrated here. I was told after she was gone." He took a couple of moments to compose himself. "When I joined this company, my first trip brought me to New Westminster. By pure chance, we literally bumped into each other."

"How do you mean?"

"I mean I was walking down this street, and she emerged from a shop door and I knocked the bags from her hand."

"Wow. And what happened?"

"Neither of us believ..." "He began. "Never mind what fucking happened next. None of your fucking business!"

"Come on Ricky, you can't leave it there. This is the first time you've gone into detail over any woman. I'm getting excited."

"Cheeky bastard!" He raised his hand as if to slap Stevie, then declined. Looking at his watch, he said, "She'll be here in 30 minutes. I want you to promise me you'll stay dumb, cocaine is nothing to joke about, especially here. Promise me!"

Stevie nodded.

"Not good enough, say it!"

"I promise."

"Leave now, I'll bring her to your cabin when she arrives."

Stevie must have hit a raw nerve. Ricky certainly still had feeling for her. Stevie felt a little ashamed and pitiful at the same time, he waited with anticipation to meet her.

"Come in." Stevie answered to the knock.

Following behind Ricky, entered an ageing hippy fanatic. She stood 5ft. 9ins tall in her platform ankle boots. She wore a long flowery dress that shimmered in the light, a baggy flowing dress which somehow suited her. She had dimples each side of full shiny pink lips, they made her look so cute when she smiled. A long nose gave her a Jewish look. Her high cheek bones seem to widen her deep blue eyes with just the right amount of make up to hide the ageing bags and wrinkles under them. Her silky brown wavy hair, tied in a pony tail hung down her back to her waist. Her 40 years suited her well. She was attractive, and 20 years ago, she must have looked stunning.

"Stevie, this is Nora."

"Pleased to meet you Stevie. I hope Ricky's not teaching you bad ways?" We shook hands and embraced each other. Her smile was warm and inviting.

"Hi Nora, only good ones." We all laughed.

Ricky said. "Nora and I are going ashore, she brought some weed." He handed Stevie a bag. "See you tomorrow."

"Don't smoke it all, leave some for later." Nora demanded, she smiled as the two left.

The next morning, after breakfast, Stevie found himself on deck, watching huge sucking machines gradually remove sugar from the hatches. Eleven days to load; three to unload.

A car pulled up beside the gangway and Ricky got out the passenger side. Stevie watched them kiss goodbye before Ricky closed the door and Nora drove away. He stood for several moments, turned, and began boarding.

"Everything okay Ricky? You look upset." Stevie asked with a concerned look on his face meeting him at the top of the gangway.

"I couldn't feel better. We're sorted! Someone will be boarding tonight and business will be completed. See you later."

Not seeing Ricky for the rest of the day, he entered Stevie's cabin late that evening.

"Well how did it go?" Stevie asked, full of enthusiasm.

"I told you already. Like clockwork."

"I'm not talking about the drugs, I mean Nora! Did you have a good night?"

"Yeah!" One word answer.

"Is that it 'yeah', are you seeing her tonight?"

"No!" Another one word answer.

"Ricky, talk to me, you're not making sense."

Ricky took time to roll a joint. Lighting it up, and taking a couple of draws, he said. "The only woman I ever really loved, then I lost her many years ago, I see her only each time I come to Canada, and that's to deal in drugs. She lives in New Westminster. (British Columbia) I know we're heading there next, but she'll stay away."

"Why?"

"She's married with four children. Her oldest is my son"

Stevie sat gob-smacked, he felt so sorry for him, this was the first time he'd opened up his heart to anyone.

He went on. "I used to wonder often if she hadn't emigrated to Canada all those years ago, would I be her husband now? Would we be man and wife? Would her kids be our kids? Was she my soulmate? Crazy what life throws at you. If we had married, would I have joined the Navy? So many questions with difficult answers." His eyes welled up. "The French say it beautifully; *'C'est la vie'.*"

Stevie tried to console him but failed. Sniffing and wiping his eyes, he stood up. He was a hard man. "Fucking look at the state you've got me in."

"Me! Why blame me?" Stevie was shocked!

He hugged me saying, "'cause you're the son I've always wanted and that's what sons do to their dad's." He broke away.

"There, I've said it! So now you know. I'm going to crash." He turned and left. "Good night!"

* * *

Leaving Victoria at seven the next morning, the ship had to be prepared for loading twenty one thousand tons of timber, seven hours later. Every third post securing the Port and Starboard guardrails, were made of a special tempered steel, extending twelve feet above the main deck, and stretching 567ft to the Prow. These were used to secure cargo on deck. Loading began the moment the ship was berthed. Special designed trucks brought hoards of packaged lumber quayside, while conveyor cranes stack them like brickwork down the hatches. All hatches now full, the focus continued on deck till the height of the Bridge Deck was reached. Chains were then guided over the timber and secured to the extended guardrail posts. The last work was to secure a walkway from the Bridge to the Focsel Head, allowing deck crews access to the Prow. The whole process took six days.

Leaving New Westminster, the ship sailed through the Straits of Georgia. From a distance, the ship looked like a huge floating log. Six days of good weather allowed good passage south. On the seventh, the weather turned for the worst. The radio officer had received warnings of Hurricane Joanne approaching, but was forecast to miss us. Nevertheless, the crew were informed and told to batten down. On the eighth day, the swell caused the ship to pitch and roll considerably, but not to cause distress. After 6 hours, you barely noticed.

After dinner that evening, Ricky and Stevie chilled out in Ricky's cabin with a joint and a couple of beers.

Ricky produced a bag and counted 15,000 Canadian dollars. He handed me $1000.

This cocaine deal was very profitable. Maybe I misunderstood Ricky. He certainly was an expert.

"I suppose your contact will be dockside when we arrive in Liverpool" Stevie asked Ricky, throwing his empty can into the gash bucket situated by the door, he scored a hole-in-one.

"Yeah, we have to discuss that. You have to disappear in Liverpool, I don't want you involved there." He looked concerned.

"Expecting trouble?"

"No, no, nothing like that. My foreign contacts, I trust with my life, but Scousers? Normally, we dock at the timber wharfs in Middlesbrough. Just got a funny feeling 'bout this run."

"I told you, dealing in cocaine is a different ball game compared to 'weed'." Stevie hesitated. "Did you feel that?"

"Feel what?"

"She's rolled."

"She's been rolling all day..." Ricky stood to his feet.

"I know that! But she hasn't rolled back."

Just then a loud bang could be heard at a distance, and the ship lurched further to port. The gash bucket came crashing down on Stevie, spilling its contents everywhere. Alarm bells began screeching throughout the accommodation block. Deafening! Another bang, much louder than the first, this time sounding like an eruption. Struggling to get up from his daybed, Ricky managed to look out the porthole. The vision awaiting him, was both horrifying and frightening, there was a continuous stream of planks of timber rushing by. The ship was now listing dangerously at 54 degrees. Another 9 and she would capsize.

I must get to the storeroom below was my first thoughts once I'd calmed my nerves. How? I had no idea.' Hope I will live through this night.'

More banging coming from all directions as Stevie hauled himself across the deck, trying to reach the cabin door. Once there, he grabbed a secure hold, and peered up and down the alleyway. Quickly pulling his head back inside as a 56 gallon drum, which had contained soft soap from the pantry, flew by crashing against the alleyway bulkheads, spilling its slippery contents. If Stevie hadn't acted as fast as he did, he would have been decapitated. Fear took over him as he tried to make headway along the slippery alleyway. He was getting nowhere fast. Hearing screams from one of the officers' wives, Stevie found the strength to haul himself towards the accommodation staircases, where he could stand and fathom out what direction he needed to go. Shipmates rushed past in all directions as Stevie managed to stop Harry.

Frantically, he asked Harry. "What's happened? And where's Ricky?"

"He and the 2nd Officer, along with four seamen, are up top trying to get forward to assess the damage."

"I heard screaming. I was trying to head that way."

"That was Julie, she fell and sprained her ankle. Just took her to the Chief Steward. She's OK!"

"What HAS happened?" Stevie's immaturity coming to the fore.

"Not sure, looks like when the Captain ordered 'heave to', a huge wave engulfed the Prow and crashed into No1 crane, ripping it from its restraining brackets like a toy. We think it's plunged overboard snapping several chains as it tumbled into the sea. Hatches one and two are losing deck cargo. I must go!"

The Captain had sent a mayday, and was preparing to 'abandon ship', when a life boat with two deep-sea tugs arrived.

The storm abated, taking three hours to pass over. The engine had cut out, along with the generators. Orange emergency lights were few and far between casting the crew quarters into semi-darkness.

The 3rd Officer, Ricky, and his squad had managed to reach forward, they secured lines to the tugs which began the hazardous voyage towards the nearest port, the Flower Capital of the World; San Francisco!

The Sun was rising as they sailed under The Golden Gate Bridge. Still listing at 53 degrees, passing Alcatraz, heading towards Fisherman's Wharf. Timber lay haphazardly, everywhere! The scene looked like someone had emptied a box of matches, and thrown them over the Main Deck.

Stevie stood transfixed at the fantastic scenery. Tall skyscrapers loomed above the morning mist. Car horns echoing throughout the Bay collecting their customers for their morning commute.

Passing a lot of piers filled with a variety of ships, they were finally manoeuvred to what looked like a derelict wharf.

Once tied up port side, (as that was lower in the water than starboard), the Captain called a meeting for all crew members.

"I haven't received full assessment yet," he began, "but according to the bosun, we may be here for two or three weeks. You may have noticed No.1 crane has vanished, and more than half the deck timber has gone. San Francisco is not our destination, and the timber is not their cargo. They will take their time to sort out this mess, and secure it so we can carry on. Only a skeleton watch is required, I'll get the Chief Mate to organise a rota, otherwise, those going ashore can do so at their own leisure. Just be safe." He was about to dismiss everyone, when he called. "Is the store-man around?" Being small, and near the back, Stevie raised his hand to be seen. "Here Captain."

"Keep on top of supplies would you?"

"Aye aye Captain."

"Good. Take care everyone. Dismissed!"

The task ahead lay horrendous. First; what was left of the deck cargo had to be removed and re-packaged. Second; the missing and damaged guardrails had to be mended or replaced before any attempt to open the hatch covers. Third; using the ships cranes, each package of timber had to be carefully removed and all while the ship was listing. Once enough timber had been removed to allow re-stacking and arrangement for re-loading, the ship slowly returned to even keel with immense relief. 50% of the deck cargo was gone and a huge hole where No1 crane stood.

Ricky and Stevie spent the several days ashore with a troop of 'Hari Krishnas'. Four guys and six women, singing and dancing along Market Street down to Fishermen's Wharf. One of the females, Kris, had shoulder length blonde hair and beautiful blue eyes hit it off with Stevie, and spent some time together.

She stood the same height as Stevie, she had a slim petite body and loved the 'weed'. Often they got so wasted, falling asleep in each other's arms. The troop lived in a district named 'Winterland'; a hippy colony several miles from the city. At the centre piece of this hippy colony stood a huge concert hall; 'Fillmore West'. During their three week stay, Stevie and Ricky watched Grand Funk Railroad; (a hugely popular American rock band), Led Zeppelin; Canned Heat; Melanie; Crosby, Stills, Nash, & Young. Two days prior, The Rolling Stones had performed.

Finally, they set sail for Panama. The 10 day sail they encountered beautiful weather. No wind and perfectly calm seas. Kris gave Stevie some grass and it was the best he had tried yet. She also gave him her address and phone number. "If you return, call me." She said, as they kissed each other goodbye.

Ricky spoke nothing of the cocaine. Staying with hippies, I thought we could sell some. "Too risky." was all he said. He seemed depressed. Had Nora got to him? He was my adopted father, I cared for him.

* * *

Arriving at Balboa, we were told to drop anchor and await further instructions. We were eventually allowed through the Gatun Locks, the same procedure entailed. Stevie was given the opportunity to take the helm once more and add to his steering tally. The ship was still three weeks behind schedule for Liverpool, but so far they'd made good progress, gaining three days under good weather. Stevie spoke too soon, at the final loch, all six mules had their lines secured, but when the water began rushing out to lower the ship, she began listing. A cable connecting No.6 mule snapped, pulling it from its mountings and crashing into the lock.

Was this fucking ship jinxed? So much for the Yankee dockers. I began feeling nervous and worried. If the

Panamanians clamp down on the ship, they may search it.
There are still 50 kilos of cocaine on board.

Dockers were frantically running around like headless chickens. Some of the crew threw lifebelts to rescue the poor mule driver, who had crawled from the upturned mule, which now lay aft, not interrupting the lock procedure. The forward gates opened, and the remaining five mules cleared the gates. Once clear, the mules were unhitched, instead of full steam ahead, the ship was ordered to dock.

They remained there, tied up for five hours while government officials handed the Captain more heavy fines. Thankfully, no one was seriously injured. The mule driver sustained a broken ankle. And, more importantly, the ship wasn't searched.

A four day sail through the Caribbean brought them passing Cuba, then Puerto Rico. After dinner that evening, Stevie was in his cabin smoking a joint, when Ricky knocked on the door.

"Come in." He looked agitated. "What's wrong?"

"I was in the Captains' cabin when the Radio Officer brought him a telegram."

"And?" Stevie was beginning to feel just as nervous.

"You won't believe this, we've been ordered to discharge full cargo in San Juan."

"What? Where's that?"

"The Island we're just passing; Puerto Rico, we dock in four hours!

"You're taking the piss."

"Wish I was."

"And Liverpool?" Dreading the answer, "And signing off? And going home rich?" Stevie couldn't stop gibbering, "and what are we gonna do? And where do we go...?"

"Calm down Stevie, how much have you smoked?" Snatching the joint from Stevie's hand, he took several draws then said, "As soon as I discover where our next cargo is situated, I can make plans. Better prepare for docking." And he left with Stevie's smoke.

It was nightfall when the ship berthed, but the array of flood lights dockside made it feel like daytime. And the heat drained your strength. Work started immediately, a hoard of dockers and special machines, they were well equipped for removing timber.

"Going ashore tonight?" Asked Ricky, entering Stevie's cabin.

"No!" Then noticing he was agitated, Stevie said, "What's wrong Ricky? Is it Nora?"

"You seem to have this strange way of manipulating me, this weird way of squeezing the truth from me. Yes! It's Nora, I can't stop thinking of her. She was different in Victoria, distant is what comes to mind."

"Listen, I don't mean to make you feel this way," Stevie felt ashamed, that he was partially to blame for Ricky's sadness. "I don't understand how I make you feel this way, but why don't you go and get yourself together, and we'll go have a couple of beers. If you wish to get it all out, I'll listen. What do you say?"

Beyond the dock gates, Ricky and Stevie came upon loud Reggae music blasting from an open wood and bamboo low rise building. Entering, the place was packed. Ricky went first as he was bigger than me and managed to get us to the bar.

Within minutes we were surrounded by hookers of all ages, vying for our custom. One in particular caught Stevie's eye. Her body was voluptuous, her tight scanty red top struggled to contain her huge breasts. Her matching tight skirt and high heels emphasised her buttocks, the taut material straining to bursting point. Her long black hair fell to her waist in tight plaits. Her big black eyes stood out through the layers of black eye shadow and liner. Her rather large nose and nostrils covered most of her top lip. And her full sensuous lips, with black high gloss lipstick looked sexy and very inviting. She pressed herself against him, Stevie could feel her large, rock hard nipples digging into his chest as she whispered in his ear. "Hello handsome, want to buy me a drink?"

This was getting ridiculous. Rubbing her breasts into him with such vigour, he stood uncomfortable with a full erection, trying in vain to conceal it. She wouldn't leave him alone, feeling his discomfort. Stevie admitted it was his own fault, he kept refilling her glass. He didn't have a great deal of money, and he told the hooker so. She took him to a cheap hotel about a mile away, stripped him and had her way. The cost was $50. He never went ashore afterwards for the remaining three days. Instead, Stevie cleared out the store room, which was desperately needed. He also gave his cabin a good spring clean.

When the day arrived for sailing, they still had no word of where their next cargo will come from. This happens often with 'Deep-Sea-Tramps'. After a mile off shore the anchor was dropped.

Great! I thought, now's my chance for a Caribbean shark. Reef sharks are abundant here. That whore really took it out of me. I was still stinging! The first time for a while I took out my fishing gear and set it up. A few cans of beer, some pre-rolled joints, half a chicken, and my waiting began. Still quite early, twilight, occurring, I spotted movement in the water. Placing the chicken beside me, I stood and braced myself.

Three or four dorsal fins could be seen circling around the bait, but none biting. Time was passing, more and more dorsal fins appeared in the fading light, yet still no takers. Stevie was becoming more and more frustrated. Just then Ricky arrived.

"Any luck?"

"No!" He sounded annoyed. "Loads of them about, they must have already been fed, not one is taking the bait."

Suddenly, the line sprang from Stevie's grasp.

"You've got something now!" Called out Ricky as he ran to switch on the winch and lock it. Once the line took the strain, and reverse gear engaged, the line began winding in. As the head reached Stevie's position, he lunged forward, and, with all the strength he could muster, swung the grappling hook into its flesh. Ricky then did the same, the two of them managed to land it on deck.

She measured 6 meters long, with a head span of two feet.

"Definitely a reef shark, and a beauty at that." Said Ricky. Then, "Wait Stevie." He pointed to her underbelly. "We better throw her back."

"I don't understand. What is it?"

"She's pregnant!" It's true, her belly was huge. "Help me throw her back." Easier said than done. Ricky, much stronger than Stevie, struggled to get it over the gunwale, and with what strength Stevie could muster, they succeeded.

Stevie began replenishing the hook when Ricky said. "Don't bother Stevie, just got word, we're heaving to at 0600 hours, you better get some sleep, I'll need you up at 0530."

"Where are we going?"

"Hampton Rhodes, then back to Japan!"

"Coal?"

"Coal! I'll give you a hand to clean up, then I suggest you crash out."

"And Catageña?" Ricky saw my ashen face.

"You mean Rizitta?" He laughed. "Don't you think she is a sexy woman? She's quite a chick?"

"I do, but she scares me." Stevie frowned.

"She scares you?" He laughed again.

"Or should I say, her dad scares me." With that, he walked away laughing and shouting. "Get to your bed!"

Back to the dreariest place in America took six days, then our voyage to Catageña, took another nine.

"Must I come along, surely you can manage yourself?" Whinged Stevie, securing the last mooring rope.

"You want to be a smuggler, don't you?"

Stevie nodded, then braced himself for another lecture.

"Then listen to me, I want you with me. Rizitta won't touch you, I can prevent that, she treats me as her uncle. And if Rizitta doesn't touch you, Fraydo won't either.

Without much assurance Stevie asked. "How old is she? We hardly spoke a word last time, it was more action".

"Twenty I think, maybe 19. Look, be ready after dinner. I'll arrange a taxi."

'I was so relieved to find Rizitta away. An older woman served drink, I discovered later, to be her mother. After that Puerto Rican whore had her way with me, I couldn't handle Rizitta.'

As Ricky and Fraydo got up to do business, Fraydo said. "Come with us Stevie." Ricky winked at Stevie as he followed them round the back to another straw and mud built building. Inside was stack upon stack of cocaine packages.

Handing Stevie a suitcase, Ricky told him to fill it with 50 packages. Money was exchanged. As they were leaving, Fraydo called out Stevie's name. "Si" Stevie answered.

"For you!" Fraydo said as he handed him two packages. His face was a picture of confusion.

He turned to look at Ricky. "Well, that's your first step to independence. Enjoy it!" He said.

Arriving at Panama, instead of being hauled through, the ship was ordered to drop anchor. After their last visit, they caused a ruckus and now, the authorities were making them wait.

And they waited.

And they waited.

Eventually, after 36 hours, they were allowed passage. The 2nd Officer watched as Stevie steered her through for another hour. Ticking off Stevie's sheet, the 2nd Officer studied it, then handed it back to him.

He said. "Only three more hours, and you'll have your ticket and from what I've observed, you're pretty good."

"Thank you sir."

Stevie was pleased to hear they weren't going back to Nagoya, their destination was Matsuyama and Kanazawa.

At sea, you could work whatever hours you can cope with. For Stevie, he did a minimum of 18 hours per day. There were always heaving lines, or mooring ropes to splice.

Sometimes you were on painting duty, you started painting the vessel from astern, and when you reach the bow on a ship this size, it's like painting The Forth Bridge, you have to start all over again. At night when the work was finished, Stevie played chess, or a card game, but most times, he would spend time reading, until he fell asleep.

The voyage over the Pacific to Matsuyama took 26 days, progress was good thanks to perfect weather. We arrived at 1800 hours, and once the ship was tied up and the gangway secured, Ricky and Stevie headed to a pre-arranged address hoping to sell 20 kilos.

It was over a year since Ricky dealt with them. Being good friends with the Radio Officer gave him access to phone ahead.

"Couldn't speak to my contact directly." Ricky had said, "but I've been re-assured we'll be dealt with."

And they were; another £100 in Stevie's pocket. They took another taxi and headed to a snug lounge bar in the city centre. Entering through a low archway brought them into a dimly lit room with small tables surrounded by huge cushions. To one side, a small bar where waitresses scurried backwards and forwards in school girl outfits. Their too short tunics barely covering their buttocks. One gave Stevie a wink as she took their orders. Her hair, in pigtails, hung down to her knees, Stevie was fascinated. She had sexy legs and her smile was enchanting. Her slant eyes, heavy with make up to enlarge their beauty, sparkled when she smiled. Her small turned up nose enhanced her lovely facial features.

Each time she served them drinks, she would wink and smile at Stevie. It's like the Japanese whores have a sense that could detect "Cheery Boys"; virgins!

It had taken me some time to recover from that crazy Puerto Rican woman, and Rizitta had been elsewhere. I was hoping to chat up the long haired sexy waitress. My problem was I couldn't speak Japanese, and not many Japanese speak English. The length of her hair fascinated me, I wonder what she would be...

"Ricky," Stevie snapped back to reality, pleading, "when the waitress returns, would you ask her what time she finishes?

"They're just whores Stevie, they'll finish when you want them to."

"Just ask, here she comes now. Please!"

While Ricky spoke to her, she kept flashing her eyes at me and giggling. He wished he understood what they were saying. So long was her hair, it swept the floor as she bent down to answer Ricky's questioning. As she left, she kissed Stevie on the forehead and he watched her sexy bum walk away.

"Well." Stevie asked, full of excitement and enthusiasm. "What she say?"

"I don't know how you do it. I mean you're fucking ugly!" Ricky's loud and hearty laugh could be heard everywhere.

"Piss off, what did she say, bastard?"

Calming down, Ricky said. "She told me she had a client in an hour, but if you give her a couple of minutes, she will leave with you now!"

"Really?"

"Yes, really! She's cute and very sexy, I must admit you've got a cracker there. Here she comes."

Stevie turned round just as she reached the table. Her tunic was hidden by a knee length black PVC coat, shiny and shimmering each time she moved. Her slippers were replaced with black thigh boots of the same material, disappearing beneath her coat. Ricky spoke to her for several minutes, she handed him a piece of paper, then to Stevie; he said "I told her I was your father."

"Really?"

"Japanese respect their parents, and she told me she would take care of you. I asked her where she was taking you. She said home. I told her you were young, but that's why she wants you. She understands a little English, and has given me her address. Beware though Stevie, I don't want to pick you up from the gutter."

In the taxi, she clung to Stevie with all her might. Her perfume, mixed with the aroma of PVC gave him an instant hard on. (This was his first experience of a PVC fetish he was to learn about). Arriving at a block of flats, he found it difficult getting cash from his pocket. After tipping the driver, she led him through her front door. Before he could respectfully remove his shoes, she grabbed his hand and led him straight to her bedroom.

Shoving him on her bed, smothering him in kisses, Stevie managed to pull her from his lips, gathering his breath, he began to calm her down. "Wait please, I don't know your name!"

She let go. "Nozomi." (It means: Heart of Hope.). Removing her coat and boots, she indicated for Stevie to sit, saying, "Beer? Sake?"

"Do you have coffee?" His head was spinning.

"Coffee. Yes. Please remove clothes." Her knowledge of English was little, she spoke abruptly. Returning with coffee, she finished undressing him and said. "Please, five minutes." and disappeared.

Her bed was large and luxurious, taking half of the room. Two doors made of rice paper, led to a kitchen and bathroom. Her flat was small but well kept. Essence burned in all corners giving a pleasant aroma throughout. Nozomi was still in the bathroom, she'd been there over ten minutes, and Stevie was experiencing a droop. As he was about to get up to see what had happened to her, she suddenly appeared. The sight that confronted him, had him speechless. Her hair, black and shiny, released from its strains covered her from head to her knees. He'd never seen hair so long, so silky, it looked fantastic. Apart from her boots, she was naked.

As she approached, she parted her hair to reveal a red satin body suit, topless and crotchless. Her small but sturdy breasts with large rock hard nipples, soon got his cock back to full strength. She gently steered Stevie to lie on the bed while she climbed on top of him, smothering him once more with long deep kisses, her tongue searching, caressing all around the inside of his mouth, probing every crevice, interlocking their tongues. Her hair now covered both of them, its silkiness turning Stevie on incredibly. Her pussy giving him a dry fuck. She let go of his mouth, and began moving down his body, licking every inch of him, until she reached rock hard cock, she swallowed it all. He felt her tongue wrap around its length, sliding up and down as her sucking became stronger and faster till Stevie couldn't stand it anymore, he exploded like he'd never exploded before. That did not stop Nozomi, she continued sucking, and sucking, and swallowing every last drop she could squeeze out of him. Stevie had never felt such heights, this 20 something year old whore was making him feel like he had never felt before. The sexual heaven he was in, was also slightly painful, his cock had almost been rubbed away. Grabbing her hair, raising her head, he begged for her to stop.

"You like?" Her tantalising smile captivated him. She began wrapping some of her hair around his worn out looking cock. The feeling was sensational. Staring into his eyes and wiggling her tongue at him, she began wanking him off with her hair. She had his knees trapped between her booted legs preventing him from moving his lower body. Increasing the rhythm, she had his chest heaving and bouncing around with each thrust. Stevie hung onto her hair to try to steady himself, and as he was about to cum, she jumped up, and slamming her dripping wet pussy down onto his raging cock, taking the full length in one go. She ground her mouth onto his, managing to wring out another devastating orgasm.

Stevie felt like a sack of potatoes, lying helpless, covered in sweat pouring from every pore. Cupping his head in her hands, she pulled herself from him. Her hair sticking to their sweaty bodies. She kissed him again, saying. "Coffee?" and indicating with her hand for something to eat. Stevie barely nodded, he was completely knackered. After chicken and rice, they snuggled into each other beneath the satin bed sheets. She played with Stevie some more, but he was completely spent.

* * *

Stevie scrambled back on board, just in time the following morning to start work. He knew the stores were well stocked, he'd promised Ricky to help stow away mooring ropes which had been dishevelled in the Prow.

"Good night was it, Stevie? Did she drain you?" Ricky bellowed as Stevie arrived.

"She was some fucking woman."

"Costly?"

"Five thousand Yen, but she was worth it", Stevie sighed. "How was your night? Did you manage to get rid of any cocaine?"

"Five kilo, it was a struggle. There was another buyer but he looked too young, and I don't trust the young ones, remember that Stevie, the youngish are full of themselves, and, unlike the older ones, he had an attitude that stinks. The young ones are trying to take over, I've told you about the Yakuza!"

"How much is left?" The quicker they got rid of it, the more relaxed Stevie felt. He asked, "Do you know anyone in Kanazawa?"

"Yeah, she runs the best whore house in Japan." His eyes lit up. "So, better get your strength up."

Only a nine hour sail from Matsuyama, Kanazawa was a small fishing town on the North Japanese Island, at first glance approaching the wharf, the ship seemed too big to dock, but a berth, large enough to handle her was made available. Several small boats were asked to move to allow more berth space. She took up most of the harbour.

The main street of Kanazawa ran next to the main pier. A large crowd gathered to look, causing traffic jams as people stopped to learn what such a large ship, a rare occurrence, was doing here. A group of young females were waving at someone on board, Stevie looked around to see who it could be. Just as he thought, Ricky, was standing on the Bridge Deck frantically waving back.

'Must be his 'hooker' friends. I was apprehensive about the night ahead. I don't think I could handle any more whores. Maybe I'll stay aboard.'

"What do you mean you're not going ashore?" Ricky asked, entering Stevie's cabin after dinner.

"I just want a quiet night on board, catch up writing letters, etc., things like that, you know what I mean."

"The best whore house in the whole of Japan is ten minutes away." Ricky sounded excited. "And you want to stay aboard? You're fucking crazy!"

"That may be, I'm just fucked, I won't be good for anything nor anybody."

He got serious. "I want you to meet my contact, this could be my last time here."

"What are you talking about?"

"I need you with me, Stevie, please get yourself together. I'll be back in half an hour."

Stevie stood transfixed for several moments.

'Does he not listen to a word I say? Sometimes I think he's fucking deaf, or not interested in what others are saying to him.'

An hour later, Ricky and Stevie entered a single storey wooden building. They were greeted by several waitresses, all dressed in short black satin outfits. After the usual greetings and handshakes, they were led to a low table furthest away from the door. Their order of sakě was taken by one of the waitresses, who winked at Stevie. She had such a sexy smile. Already, they had exchanged shoes for slippers. The room was large, the walls made from rice paper. Stevie counted seven doors, including the one they entered. Several tables with groups of men with their Geisha escorts filled the room with laughter. When a door opened, a couple would emerge, then another couple would get up, leaving, holding hands. It was well organised. Ricky was right, this was definitely the best whore house in Japan.

Within minutes of sitting, sakě and oysters were placed on the table by two beautiful Geisha girls, dressed in long sheer silk dresses, one ice blue, the other deep green. Their hair and make-up was perfect, enhancing their beauty. They sat down and snuggled in beside Ricky and Stevie. Ricky began talking to them in Japanese.

'I've asked Ricky several times to teach me Japanese. He said it was a hard language to learn. He admitted I would need to learn at some stage, but sometimes I got the impression he doesn't want to teach me.'

Their English was poor, and Stevie had only learnt several words of Japanese, when he did speak, the whores just laughed at him. When the time came for their purchased slot to arrive, the whore in the green dress, grabbed Stevie's hand and led him through one of the doors.

The room was small, most of the space was taken up by a huge bed. A small table sat in front of a small 2-seater couch, and apart from a dumb waiter containing several popular drinks, and nibbles in one corner, left very little room to move. Like all Japanese women, they were trained from early schooling to satisfy a man. Their techniques and knowledge of the male body fascinated Stevie. Once more, he was treated like a 'God', and subject to fascinating love making. She brought him to a sensational climax twice, and began her third attempt when loud screaming stopped her.

Through the paper thin walls in an adjoining room, naked women were running around shouting and yelling words Stevie didn't understand.

Keisatsu! Keisatsu! (call the police).

Stevie jumped from the bed, grabbed his clothes, and with difficulty, managed to scramble into his denims, and run into the next room. He abruptly stopped in his tracks at the sight that lay in front of him.

Lying face down on the bed, he noticed a syringe and needle protruding from the back of one of Ricky's knees. Stevie dropped the rest of his clothes and ran towards the bed.

"Ricky!" He shouted, over and over again. "Ricky!"

There was no reply. Turning him over, Stevie noticed his skin had turned a shade of green. His eyes were closed and he was gasping for air.

"Ricky." Shaking him, shouting his name continually, still not getting response, Stevie felt his eyes burning with the tears building up. Suddenly, several medics rushed in and Stevie was hauled aside while they began their work, trying desperately to revive Ricky.

Stevie sat in one corner, watching till his eyes became misty, filling up with tears. The whore he had been with sat beside him, trying to comfort him.

'It suddenly struck me; syringe? Needle? The back of his knees? Surely not? All the time I knew him, he had kept that secret well hidden. I suppose, when I think about it, Ricky only told me what he wanted to tell me, that was the reason I believe he was the number one smuggler throughout the seven seas! I felt privileged and honoured to have known him, for him to teach me the ropes, to pass on his knowledge to me. I quickly learnt his ways.

I'd already lost one dad, please not another? Life can be so cruel at times. What am I going to tell Nora? "He died in a whorehouse?" No! I don't think that's a good idea.My thoughts turned to fears; "What if the police search the ship? They know Ricky never obtained the drugs from the whore house!" Oh shit!!!

The ambulance sped through the town, but Ricky was pronounced dead on arrival.

Stevie was placed in the back of a police car, not understanding a word the police were saying to him, the Madam of the whore house spoke a little English and managed to explain to Stevie an interpreter would be at the station, his statement would be taken there. He wasn't handcuffed, nor treated disrespectfully. A blood test was taken, it showed traces of cannabis, but more importantly, in his defence, backing up his story, Stevie was clean of heroine.

"Where did your friend get the heroine?"

I explained to the Chief that I'd known Ricky for over two years, and never saw him inject himself with that foul drug. I told him that we usually smoke some cannabis together before going ashore, but never at sea while working on duty.

"As you are a guest in our country," the interpreter translated the police chief's words, "A seaman aboard a ship which is docked here in my city, I'm going to release you. There are no charges against you."

"Thank you sir." Stevie felt choked up.

"I will speak with your captain tomorrow. You may go!"

"Am I able to call a taxi?" Stevie asked.

The interpreter ordered for him.

The next day on board, Stevie was summoned to the Captain's office. The police chief was present along with another officer.

"Sit down Stevie." The Captain indicated towards an arm chair. "Ricky spoke highly of you. Said you were a grafter, eager to learn, and would go far. You were fond of him, yes?"

"Yes sir."

"You have my sympathy."

"Thank you sir."

"I have spoken extensively with the police chief here. I have asked him if he will release Ricky's body to me, explaining we will bury him at sea. He has agreed."

"I have his personal items. His file is vague, no mention of any family. How long have you sailed with him?"

"Eighteen months sir."

"Have you met his family?"

"As far as I know sir, he had none, apart from a woman he introduced me to in New Westminster when we were last there, sir. They were high school sweethearts. She is the mother of his son, sir."

"We sail tomorrow for Canada. I'm arranging for him to be buried at sea, we will have a service for him." We sat in silence for some time. Then, "There are phone numbers in his personal book," He handed Stevie the notebook. "Is her number here?"

"Yes sir."

"Can you contact her again?"

"Yes sir."

The Captain handed Stevie Ricky's belongings. "You can keep those. Once again, my deepest sympathies."

Turning to the police chief, he asked. "Have you any questions for Stevie?"

The chief looked at Stevie for several minutes, then back to the Captain and shook his head.

"Dismissed Stevie."

"Thank you sir!"

Twenty four hours after sailing, all hands stood on the Main Deck in silence, Stevie was given the honour of lowering Ricky's Red Ensign encased coffin into the water. Thoughts entered his head to when his real father was killed.

'I was informed he died instantly, yet, the last time on leave, I discovered his life support was turned off after three days in hospital. Why did they lie to me? Was it because Mam didn't want us to see him in hospital? It must have been so heartbreaking for Mam! To lose your soul mate!'

After dinner that night, Stevie was told by Gary, now acting bosun, to clear out Ricky's large cabin.

'Thank God for that. It'll give me a chance to find Ricky's stash. I wondered why Ricky wouldn't tell me where his hiding place was, in case of emergencies like this.....(Still, who could have predicted Ricky's death?) And now I had to find it.'

He had a day room, bedroom, shower, and office. Stevie went through every place possible, his bed, clothes cupboards, every locker, every nook and cranny, and much more. He did find a couple of ounces of grass, but no cocaine. He knew Ricky had at least 30 kilos of the drug still unaccounted for. Stevie rattled his brain to think of any place Ricky had mentioned, but nothing came to light.

An hour passed, and Stevie settled to the fact the drugs weren't here. He cleaned and tidied up the cabin. Luckily, Gary had decided not to move in, which gave Stevie more time to go over Ricky's cabin at a later date, the drugs must be somewhere! As he was leaving, and about to lock up, his left foot snagged on a crease in the carpet. He kneeled down and tugged at the crease until it gave way.

Removing the carpet aside, Stevie discovered a makeshift cover, loosely sealed. He managed to remove the cover exposing the illusive drug. With a slight nod and smile on his face with relief, he replaced the cover and carpet, making it look like new, and left with the intention of returning later.

The 12 day voyage to New Westminster encountered two bad storms which slowed the ship down somewhat. Stevie did his job, and helped Gary with painting and repairing mooring ropes. Apart from meal times, and speaking only when needed, he kept a low profile, staying in his cabin when not working. His mind was like a plate of scrambled egg, he needed to get his act together. He had cocaine to get rid of, and he had to confront Nora!

Arriving 22 hours late, the moment the ship docked at the timber quays, the loading began. Although the ship had been damaged in hurricane Julienne, she was still capable of carrying 1900 tons.

Stevie called Nora immediately the ship was tied up.

"I'll pick you up in an hour." She said.

Stevie had already packed the cocaine in a holdall several days before, but was undecided what to do with it. Nora arrived on time, and took him to a cafe she knew, ordered just coffee, they sat in a window seat.

She wore a blue trouser suit, tailor made for her, and a cream silk blouse. She wore light make up, her long hair styled in a plait down her back. She was an attractive woman, old enough to be Stevie's mum. She had picked him up straight from work!

After short greetings, she asked the inevitable. "Where's Ricky?"

Stevie took her hands in his, and held them tightly.

"While unloading in Kanazawa, a mooring rope snapped, Ricky hadn't time to jump clear, the rope caught him and threw him several yards in the air dropping him between the ship and pier."

He felt her hands gripping his tighter, shaking, getting hot and sweaty.

"By the time we got to him, he had no pulse."

She was now sobbing, tears pouring down her cheeks. Stevie moved round beside her, he held her. He was only 17 years old, how could he possibly know how to comfort a woman.....especially one who was a lady, and not a whore!.

She fell into his arms, clutching tightly, her head on his shoulder. She was heavy and sweating, Stevie's t-shirt getting wet with her tears. He'd never experienced this emotion before, he was speechless, and after several minutes, he called her name, managing to separate them.

"Nora." Stevie repeated, handing her hankies. "Here, dry your eyes. I don't know what to say."

Eventually she lifted her head, looking at him with tear stained eyes, she said. "I loved him, Stevie. I was so upset when my parents decided to move out here. I was pregnant at the time with his son."

"Ricky told me a little about you, and the circumstances surrounding your farewell. He loved you Nora, and when you left, he decided to join the Merchant Navy to drown his sorrows."

Stevie slid the holdall towards her.

"What's this?" She asked.

"30 kilos of cocaine. I don't know what to do with it. I'm sure Ricky would have wanted you to have it."

"But I don't have any cash with me."

"That's okay! I can't get rid of it, I'm sure you can."

"When do you sail?" She'd managed to compose herself.

"In three days. Why?"

"I'll try and see you before you leave."

We finished our coffee, and Nora took me back to the ship.

Two days later, Gary informed Stevie a woman was asking for him quayside. It was Nora!

Stevie climbed into her car and they greeted each other with a friendly kiss.

"Hello Stevie." She said, handing me an envelope, "that's all I've managed to get rid of."

He counted $1500. (Canadian). He took $500, and handed the envelope back to Nora.

"No Stevie, that's yours, it's the best I can do with such short notice. I still have 14 kilos to sell."

"You're okay then Nora?"

"I'm fine!" She opened her purse and produced Ricky's personnel things. "Take these, they're no good to me, I have my own memories of him."

They kissed once more and said their goodbyes.

They never met again!

The ship sailed at dawn on schedule the following day, a 10 day voyage to Panama lay ahead. Arriving Bilbao on time for bunkers, docking on the starboard side, the operation was scheduled for 8 hours.....Or should have been, but an outlet valve on the port side had not been secured correctly.

As a result, it took 3 hours before someone realised the fuel was being pumped straight through the ship, and into the water. All hell broke loose not just with the Captain, but the authorities had been informed, and the Captain was issued with a $5,000 fine, plus payment for the clean-up.....A total of $12,000. When the time came to sail, they were told to remain at anchor till further notice. The ship was allowed to sail after two more days. Two weeks later, they arrived five months behind schedule at Queen Victoria Docks, Liverpool.

The ship had been at sea when the British Government changed the hundreds of years old currency £SD, to the new decimal currency. Therefore, Stevie collected two wage packets: one pre-February in 'old money', the second in 'new money'.

For the first time in many years, Stevie was looking forward to going home! So much so, he ordered a taxi. When it arrived quay side, and before Stevie placed his luggage in the boot, he asked the taxi driver; "How much to Whitehaven?"

"Where?" The driver seemed confused.

"Whitehaven, West Cumbria."

The driver began a sarcastic giggle. "Yeah, right mate, taking the piss, are we?"

"I'm serious. Look!" Stevie took out a bag from his holdall, produced a wad of notes, handed it through the door window and said, "£100, are you up for it?"

The taxi driver looked at the cash for several moments, and said, "Put your bags in the boot!"

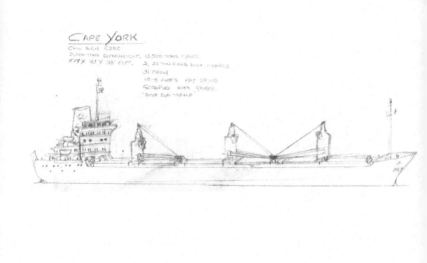

CAPE YORK

CALL SIGN GZOC
21,000 TONS DEADWEIGHT, 11,500 TONS GROSS
527 X 73 X 33' FEET.   2, 32 TON COMB. DECK CRANES
                        31 CREW
                        15·5 KNOTS MAY SPEED
                        SCRAPPED 1999 CHINA
                        "OUR SHIP TODAY"

GLASGOW
LONDON   AMSTERDAM

                                    SINGAPORE

                    NAIROBI
                    MOMBASA
                                              CHRISTMAS ISLAND   CAIRNS
                                                    SYDNEY
                    FREMANTLE   PORT PIRIE   WOLLONGONG
                              PORT LINCOLN   MELBOURNE   AUCK

Chapter Four
M.V. Cape York

The summer of '71 was one of those years you want to forget. The occasional glimpse of the sun between days of wind and rain making it one of the wettest on recorded history. Staying with his mum for two weeks did not lighten his mood.

School friends had long gone by now, either in a deep relationship, or moved from the area. So he decided he would buy the BSA Lightning he had promised himself some years ago.

On that Monday morning, an argument erupted, his mum going on and on about the dangers of the road and so on.

'Dangers? Mam, you have no idea the dangers I face every day at sea!. I couldn't tell her, nor any of my family about my smuggling, and besides, why should I? I'd learnt from Ricky to tell people only things you want them to know, that way, no one knew any difference. I missed Ricky, without him, what was I going to do? Yes, he had introduced me to certain people, but I was far too young to take on the kind of big time smuggling he had taught me.

By myself, it was going to be very difficult, maybe it's time to stop! I've made a good deal of money, more than I could imagine. So far, I've got away with it.'

Stevie loved the sun with all the heat it radiated, he believed he was a Druid in a past life. With the miserable weather, he longed to be back at sea. He missed the sun, the thought of a further three weeks at home upset him.

One day, he took the liberty of phoning head office.

"You've still three weeks leave remaining Stevie." Said Peter, the personnel manager, "What's wrong? Are you bored?"

"A little." I answered.

"Let me check." He went through shipping schedules. "There's nothing really available just yet, and there're others who are just coming off leave, they have priority."

"I'll take on anything Peter, please, I'm begging you."

"You've just come off the Baron Forbes, I was sorry to hear about Ricky McEwen, I heard you and he were good friends."

"It got to me for sure, but life goes on.. I miss him, I think of him often, but I'm over the shock now."

There was a moment of silent reflection, then Stevie said, "Is there anything at all?"

"Have you heard of the 'Cape' boats?"

"Only what I've read in the Triad. Are they the Baron boats' sister ships?"

"In a way, Scottish Ship Management, who we are, run their schedules. They are owned by Lyle Bros. of Glasgow."

A moment of silence, then Peter went on. "Did your training include any catering duties?"

"I spent six months in the galley, at Indefatigable, if that's what you mean? Why do you ask?"

"There's a position for a second cook and baker on the Cape York. Will that interest you? The salary is the same as a storeman!"

"Yes, That sounds perfect, please tell me the details."

"She's unlike the 'Tramps', she's sub-contracted to the Australian Phosphate Commission, and has been since she was launched in 1968. Her three month round trip loads phosphate in Christmas Island for ports in Australia. Then she loads grain for human consumption, and ships that to Mombasa, Kenya, then back to Christmas Island for phosphate, and so on, you get the picture."

"Sounds great." Stevie said, "how long is the trip?"

"Six months, that's two round trips taking 3 months each."

"I'll take it, when and where do I join her?" Stevie was getting very excited, he just wanted to get away.

"You'll fly out to Amsterdam on Wednesday evening, you'll be met at the airport. There will be 12 of you. You'll stay overnight, then fly out to Singapore at 7am, arriving Thursday morning. Any questions?"

"Sounds like a long flight. Where should I pick up my tickets?"

"One of the longest I believe; 23 hours. Call into the office on Tuesday morning, after 10. I'll leave them with Lorna along with any other details you may need. I'm off on holiday, so have a good voyage."

"Thank you Peter, that's one I owe you. You have a lovely holiday, and take care." He hung up.

Two days later, Stevie flew out of Glasgow airport at 4 pm, landing at Amsterdam 45 minutes later. Clearing customs and immigration, he was met by an attractive young woman holding a placard with the words 'Cape York'. He approached her and she asked his name, ticking a box on her list. She then introduced herself as Helen, the company rep in Amsterdam.

"There are seven others," she said in a beautiful Dutch accent. "Have you met any?"

He was just about to answer no, when two burly fellows arrived at their side. Each gave their name to the lovely Helen, then introduced themselves to Stevie.

Matt, a 27 year old, stood over six feet three inches of solid muscle, his shoulder length light brown hair hung loose, he was constantly flicking his head to clear his face of hair, that was beginning to look like a permanent twitch. His huge square shaped jaw suited him and when he smiled, everyone around automatically did the same without thinking. He was one of the ABs (Able-bodied seaman).

Willie, the 32 year old chief cook, and Stevie were to work together in the galley. Willie, from Shetland stood the same height as Stevie at 5ft. 7ins. They were to have many a dispute as to who was the tallest.

Another typical Scotsman, thick wavy ginger hair cut below his ears in a conservative hairstyle. He sported a ginger moustache which always needed trimming. Deep blue eyes set close together above a bright red nose, he was nick named Rudolf. Stevie and he were to become not just good shipmates, but really good friends.

Stevie soon discovered both Matt and Willie were also partial to a little 'weed'.

Within minutes, another 5 arrived. After ticking off their names, Helen led them all out to an awaiting minibus.

Once everyone was seated, Helen instructed the driver to take them to the 'Broadway Hotel'.

After checking in the hotel, and having had something to eat, Willie, Matt and Stevie decided to head into the city for a couple of beers, and maybe a couple of joints. They were due to fly to Singapore at 7am, so a couple of beers were all they decided to have. They needed an early night, and a good sleep.

No fucking chance! This was fucking Amsterdam! A gutsy feeling told me this voyage would go down in history. I looked forward to it with great anticipation.

Visiting several coffee shops, and without realising the strength of the grass on offer, they wanted to try anything and everything. It was not long until Stevie was completely wasted. He had smoked three joints and was destined to belong to anyone who could pick him up out of the gutter.

It was good to meet two shipmates who enjoyed a toke as much as Stevie did. Yes, on the other ships, he had Ricky and the others, but joining a new boat with a fresh crew would take a lot of sussing out who to trust.

Willie decided, as he was the eldest in age and rank, to take it on his own head to watch, and take care of Stevie.

"How old are you?" He asked Stevie, passing him a joint, his deep blue eyes glazed over completely.

"Eighteen".

"Wow! I wish I was your age again. Are you a virgin?"

"Pardon! "

Just then, 4 young Dutch ladies walked through the door, and before they had time to reach a table, Matt stood up and bellowed. "Over here girls." Waving his arms frantically.

Needless to say, in the morning, they arrived at the hotel just in time for a quick breakfast and clean up. All eight relief crew members gathered in the hotel foyer but Helen was nowhere to be seen. Then, the driver arrived and ushered them all onto the minibus for the journey to the airport.

Stevie's head was spinning with every slight movement, the pain was killing him. Never before had he felt so bad in the morning. He usually held his drink quite well. With a lack of sleep, and a parched throat with all the singing and shouting that had occurred the previous night, Stevie's eyes were meeting, they felt very heavy, and it wasn't long into the flight before he fell into sleep once again.

Disturbed only once when the plane landed at Damascus for fuel, Stevie slept most of the flight. Bangkok was the second stop several hours later, also for fuel, so Stevie decided to stretch his legs for the ten minutes you were allowed.

Three hours later, at 0615 hour, they landed in Singapore where they were met by the company rep in Singapore, Margie. Again, they boarded a minibus, and were transported to a hotel. When questioned why they weren't going to the ship, Margie replied that the ship had been delayed.

"She was due in yesterday, but now, she's not expected until the day after tomorrow." They checked into the Hotel Malena, and within 15 minutes Stevie had fell asleep.

Awakened some hours later by Matt, who almost fell over him storming into the room and shouting "Quick! Get up and get your ass together! We're going out!"

"What time is it?" Stevie yelled, struggling to open one eye and get himself together.

"It's 1130. Here, take a puff of this." Matt stuffed a lit joint into Stevie's mouth before he could say any more. "I've never had anything like this before!" Stevie's senses began to kick in, he took a couple of long draws on the joint, and kept it in as long as he could. Minutes later his head was spinning. "Jeeechhh!" Stevie blurted out, coughing and spluttering, "Where did you get this shit, I'm buzzing already!"

"While you were sleeping, Willie and I spent the last 3 hours in a small bar just 50 metres from here. We got talking to a couple of whores when one produced this red cotton material, she began skinning up."

"What is it?" Stevie coughed and spluttered out.

"Don't waste it," Called Willie, entering the room, "cost a fucking fortune."

"OK, but what the fuck is it? I enjoy a smoke, but I like to know what I'm inhaling."

"Fucking good shit eh? Come on", Willie cried out, "get your act together, we're going back to that bar after dinner. Fancy?"

"Sure, after dinner, see you then."

As they left, Matt handed a little of whatever it was over to Stevie, who immediately skinned up and smoked it.

The three of them, Matt, Willie, and Stevie all met in the lobby at 8pm, and after a five minute walk, they entered 'The Goose's Neck'.

Weird name for a pub I thought, especially in Singapore. It's my first time here, I was looking forward to the experience. Who am I to criticize?

The lounge bar was crowded and took some time to squeeze their bodies through to the bar, where they ordered three rounds a piece.

"No point in queuing every time we need to be replenished." Said Willie, "Let's get drunk!"

While waiting, Stevie noticed the most beautiful dark haired woman staring at him. Her eyes, were slightly Asian, dark, oval, and set wide apart. Heavy black make up and false lashes making her dark eyes appear larger, hypnotising the looker, they drew you into her depths. Her eyes had Stevie hooked, he was having difficulty diverting his own eyes away from hers. She stood at least 4 inches taller than him, though she wore very high black come to bed stilettos. Her lips were sensuous, pouting and shone with dark red lipstick. Her black shiny hair reached half way down her back. The red satin halter neck jumpsuit she wore barely covered her sexy body. That was nothing compared to her enormous breasts. She had the kind that would poke your fucking eyes out. At one moment, they were about to burst out the tight flimsy material that covered them.

The tables were partitioned and enclosed for privacy, Willie chose near the rear.

Matt had also spotted those tits and was frantically waving her over. Stevie watched in awe as she, and three of her friends approached their table.

"Please sit down." Gestured Matt, and called a waitress who was just passing, "drinks all round."

Somehow all 4 women managed, with great difficulty, to squeeze into the cubicle where they sat.

Stevie turned to Willie, "What's he doing? They're hookers, and I've no money for that!"

"Just relax! And go with the flow."

"OK for you to say, but this one beside me won't stop playing with my dick."

Willie laughed. "So what's the problem?"

"Her fucking nipples, that's the fucking problem, are literally poking into my chest. I just cannot stop looking at them." Stevie stopped short as he felt her breath in his ear. Her perfume caused Stevie almost to climax there and then as she rubbed his crotch.

"You feel nice." She said, wriggling her tongue in his ear.

"Please, your name? My name Nikki." Again, her tongue darting in and out of his ear.

"Stop that, you're driving me fucking nuts!"

"Me like nuts!" And politely squeezed his balls.

Stevie's dick felt so hard, it was about to burst his fly's wide open. Damp patches were appearing causing much discomfort.

She asked. "Are you a cherry boy?"

"I'm sorry. A what?"

"You cherry boy!"

Stevie noticed the others looking.

"She wants to know if you're a virgin." Laughed Matt.

"I told you Stevie, to go with the flow." Said Willie. He nodded his head several times.

"Ah Stevie," Nikki purred. "Me fuck loonnnggg time."

That was last straw. Stevie immediately came in his denims.

'A Cherry Boy was the term used by South East Asian prostitutes for a virgin. If they find one, the Cherry Boy gets a free night with all expenses paid; in other words, a night of passion.

(At this rate I'll be spent before I get to bed)'

Shortly afterwards, Stevie found himself in a taxi with Nikki, still rubbing his cock, like there was no tomorrow. Soon, they arrived at a hotel of her choosing. Hotel Golf, nothing too fancy but clean, and besides, she was paying.

Stevie thought he'd lost his virginity at the age of 14, by an older woman *who had* cornered him at the local swimming pool, she managed to get his cock between her bikini bottoms and her pussy, Stevie believed that was him losing my virginity. In Osaka, the three Geishas had taken his virginity for sure. He could not claim he was a "cherry boy" any more.

Once they booked into the room, Stevie rushed straight to the loo, hoping to calm down his raging tool. When he returned, she had stripped and was lying under the covers, smiling and egging him on to join her. So much for trying to cool down! Stevie stripped and joined her.

They began kissing and cuddling immediately, he could feel her hand grab a hold of his dick with such force, Stevie thought she was trying to yank it off. So he I responded with kind, slowly moving his hand over her magnificent breasts, the nipples standing out like two sore thumbs, longing to be tweaked and fondled.

Moving down her smooth stomach till he reached her crotch, sliding his hand down between her luscious thighs, his hand became soaking wet with the juices running from her. Suddenly, he froze! To his utter shock, he discovered that she not only had a very wet pussy, but a huge dick made worse by the fact it was bigger than Stevie's. That itself was enough for Stevie to worry about, when he looked back at her face, she was smiling, egging him to join. Stevie jumped up from the bed, and just stared at her/him or whatever she/he was.

I'd heard of 'dick-girls'. The term I believe is "Hermaphrodite". I thought that was a myth. I suddenly realised I'd spent my first night in Singapore, sporting a raging hard-on over a fucking 'dick-girl'. I don't think I have ever been so disgusted in all my life. I was so angry with myself to think my dick had longed for her...I mean him...all night. I thought of.

Willie and Matt; those bastards knew. Hope they got a good laugh out of it. Wait till I get back on board. I lashed out at the 'dick-girl' and caught him on the chin, then booted him in his groin. He went down in agony. I grabbed him by his beautiful hair and threw him onto the landing. I don't know what happened to him after that, I didn't care! I was out of there like a bullet. I don't think I have ever been so disgusted in all my life.

I was so angry with myself to think I'd had a raging hard-on for her... I mean him... all night. I'll need to think more with my head and not my cock! I mean what if I had submitted to her(his) whims. The thought disgusted me. It put me off. Then again, I might have enjoyed it. I mean, I had just turned 18, what if I liked it?

* * *

The ship arrived the next morning and berthed at the fuel bunker wharf. Then Margie had gathered everyone in the hotel lobby after dinner. She looked confused "Are we all here? We seem short."

Hamish the cook, raised his hand. "He was with us last night, he met someone and left with her."

"Really? Don't you think you should have stayed with him, after all, he's just a boy!"

Looking at Matt, Hamish replied, "I'm sure he's in good hands." They all burst into a fit of laughter.

Just then, Stevie entered the lobby and headed straight to Matt with a raised voice.

"You fucking shower of bastar..." I stopped dead realising everyone in the lobby was staring at me, including Margie.

She sounded concerned, "Are you Okay?" Checking her list, she asked, "Stevie is it?"

"Yes!"

"Okay, we're all present and correct. Please everyone follow me."

The mini bus took them to the quay side where the ship was berthed.

Re-fuelling took twelve hours by which time Stevie had settled into his cabin and he stayed there, too embarrassed to face anyone. He gave Willie and Matt a piece of his mind. Then they just laughed it off.

"Didn't you click on to the Adam's Apple?" asked Matt.

"No, what about the Adam's Apple?"

"Didn't you know it's prominent in men, difficult to see in women."

"No, I didn't! She, or fucking HE wore a choker round HIS fucking neck. I'll take it as a learning curve eh? You pair of bastards!"

They all had a good laugh. It was the only sensible thing to do!

An hour later, he watched the lights of Singapore vanish over the horizon. Four days later they arrived at Christmas Island to load 25,000 tons of phosphate bound for Wollongong (New South Wales), Cairns (Queensland), and Port Pirie (South Australia).

The first thing he noticed as the main island came into view was the ship was almost as big as the island itself from a distance of several nautical miles away. How on earth, he thought, are they going to load a full cargo when he could not even make out a town or docks, or anywhere that could hold a ship of this size.

The pilot boarded and guided them through a narrow channel till they reached several buoys. Small power boats then gathered their mooring lines and secured them to the buoys till the ship lay perfectly still. To the port side was a small beach with a dozen or so wooden buildings scattered here and there. It looked like all the inhabitants were lined up shore side.

On the starboard side was nothing but a sheer rock face rising out of the water. Stevie wondered how they were going to load when a loud hum behind the cliff face answered the question. Engines started and gears crunched.

He stood in amazement as part of the rock face descended into the water. From within came two large conveyor belts protruding towards the hatches. Once they reached a precise spot, they began pouring tons upon tons of phosphate into the holds. It poured in so fast Stevie watched the ship sunk slowly into the sea. The noise was unbearable, and the dust cloud it created covered the entire ship with brilliant white powder. It made it very difficult to keep his eyes open. The brightness was so intense. The whole process took under twelve hours. No chance of getting ashore to taste the culture, or smoke the grass. And then, once again they were back on the high seas.

They arrived in Cairns (Queensland) eight days later, unloaded about half the cargo which took three days, and sailed to Wollongong (New South Wales). Another 5,000 tons were discharged. That took six days, the unloading system there was much slower, and finally onto Port Pirie (South Australia). A much smaller place. In fact the ship could barely dock alongside. A lot of time was spent manoeuvring her into position until finally, the gangway was erected.

Most of the inhabitants from town were alongside to greet them, after all it was not often a ship of this size docked in their port. They used the ship's cranes to unload, but each could only manage 1,000 tons per day. Once unloaded, they set sailed for Port Lincoln (South Australia), a mere twelve hours away. In which time the hatches were to be cleaned to the point of spotless, to load 20,000 tons of grain for human consumption bound for Mombasa (Kenya). Only twelve hours to sanitise the hatches. Everyone was on their hands and knees mucking in, including the skipper who was often seen scrubbing like there was no tomorrow. (Must be on a bonus!).

Eighteen hours later they set sail for Mombasa (Kenya), stopping at Freemantle (Western Australia) for engine fuel (bunkers)!

Fifteen days later they arrived in Mombasa. The voyage across the Indian Ocean was the calmest fifteen days they spent at sea. The weather was glorious the entire trip.

Stevie befriended a couple of albatrosses, Cheech & Chong, he named them. Every morning when he woke up and ventured out on deck for a stretch and a bit of fresh air, there they were, gliding through the sky effortlessly, watching him, waiting for their first feed of the day. Whatever was left in the galley trash buckets, Stevie threw over the side, which within minutes, Cheech & Chong devoured it all. They would eat anything!

They say an albatross protects seamen. They say if you don't encounter an albatross while sailing the southern oceans, your trip is doomed! Old seaman's tales, Stevie presumed. Even so, he was glad to see them each morning. The day before they docked was the last he saw of them.

He was called as usual at 6am the morning they docked. First thing that hit him was the silence. The only audible sound was the low hum of generators, which was nothing compared to the constant turning of the ship's engines. After a shower and the usual ablutions, Stevie went up to the pantry for breakfast and bumped into Willie (whom Stevie called 'Hashish'). The chief cook was singing to himself as he poured coffee.

"Won the pools?" Stevie asked.

"Chance is a fine thing!" He laughed. "Can't wait to clock off and get ashore. I haven't been here for a couple of years now, you're always sure of a good time."

Stevie told him it was his first visit.

"You stick with me tonight, I'll show you around." He then disappeared into the galley.

Stevie grabbed a cuppa, a couple of croissants, and went out on deck. The heat took his breath away. It was already 22 degree Celsius at 0700 hour. In the distance he could see Mombasa's skyline. Not very impressive as most of it was obscured by trees. One or two high-rise office blocks appeared here and there. Trails of smoke rose up periodically through the greenery. The ship was berthed at the end of a long pier, about two or three miles from the city. What looked like a highway ran off at the other end of the pier and ran through what looked like some sort of shanty town. Buildings made of wood, corrugated tin and canvass laid scattered along this highway. He counted 6 large crab cranes, three were already alongside manoeuvring large funnels to suck the grain from each hold.

A convoy of old shabby trucks already waiting in line for the cargo. The ship's cranes were unhitched, their beams hanging over the side to allow shore side cranes access to the hatches. What took a mere 34 hours to load was going to take two weeks to discharge using small mechanical pumps to suck grain out of the hatches.

The first night ashore, several of the crew visited a local bar, yards from the dock gates. There were plenty of young ladies present, all trying to catch a sailor to spend the night with. They were all on the game.

Stevie spotted one in particular, not as attractive as some, but possessed a body to die for! Her name was Darlina. She looked like a Zulu Goddess. Tall, 5ft.10in with legs that went on forever. Huge black pouting lips below high cheek bones, short stubby nose and large black eyes set wide apart. She wore a long auburn wig as she was embarrassed with her tight and curly hair. He guessed her age to be 26. She drove him back to her place; a red brick bungalow, concealed by a three foot wall circulating her home made of the same red brick.

Passing through a lobby, she led Stevie into a large living room. Expensive wall decorations and ornaments lined the walls. Large plush rugs donned the wooden flooring. Partitioned off with colourful expensive curtains between two pillars, laid a king size bed, neatly prepared and covered with satin sheets. Another closed off area was the kitchen, all the mod cons apparent, the aroma drifting from within making him hungry. In the central area, also partitioned off, laid a low coffee table surrounded by two leather couches. She had expensive tastes and he started to wonder how much she would cost, hoping he had sufficient funds.

"Give me your jacket." She said, her big dark eyes penetrating mine. "Please make yourself comfortable. Can I get you something to drink?" She had a good knowledge of English.

"Love the smell from the kitchen. What is that?"

"That's breakfast, and that's later!" She disappeared behind the bedroom curtain. Time was passing. Now midnight, he was due on shift at 0800 hour and she seemed to be away for ages. He was about to call her when she emerged from the curtain.

First he noticed she'd removed her wig, and yes, her hair was short and tight and curly. But it didn't diminish her beauty. Her dark eyes appeared wider. She changed into an expensive green silk nightdress. A floor length halter-neck with shoestring straps tied round her neck. The neckline plunged down to her narrow waist, concealing not much more than her nipples. She wore a matching robe over it. His dick hardened suddenly.

Holding out her hand, she coaxed. "Come, your bath is ready."

She washed every square inch of his body professionally, taking special care around his crotch, making sure he did not wane.

"If you keep that up," he protested, "I'll be spent too early."

She reached forward, stuck her tongue in his ear and said, "No you won't. I'll make sure of that!"

Thirty minutes later, using her thighs as a vice, her hands squeezing his breasts she pinned him to her bed. "Don't you dare move an inch."

Positioning her pussy lips on his dick, she slowly lowered herself taking the foreskin with her till she swallowed only his bell-end. The immense thrill made Stevie lift his hips, trying to force himself into her dripping pussy. She suddenly let him go. "I told you not to move!"

"Sorry can't help it, you're driving me nuts!"

"Just relax Stevie, I'm going to blow your fucking mind!" With that she returned to gripping my bell-end and began rocking to and fro. Very slow to start, gradually picking up speed. Her large breasts and rock-hard nipples smashing into his face. Stevie's dick was barely inside her yet, within minutes he came, and he couldn't stop. Thrashing and squirting everywhere. One movement forced his dick to fall out, the next she engulfed him. This continued for some time, he began to feel pain shooting through his groin till it was unbearable.

"Stop!" he shouted. Her grip left him helpless. She was so engrossed in her orgasm Stevie was convinced she had forgotten he was there. "Please, Darlina, stop!"

She heard and thankfully slowed down. She collapsed on him, kissing wildly as she calmed down. Coated in sweat, she slithered from the bed and headed for the bathroom.

'I'd *never* felt anything like that. Still, I'd not long lost my virginity, I am still learning! I doubt any of my sperm entered her. Her method prevented impregnation. She was a professional!'

After showering, she poured a shukichie, he was sure it was spiked. Returning to bed Stevie said, "You are amazing! How much do you cost?"

"Whatever you think I'm worth." She smiled showing her perfect white teeth in contrast to her ebony skin, her big eyes sparkling. "We'll discuss that later."

"More than I can afford for sure." He just wanted to sleep. She tried to arouse him but realising he was spent, she got up and left.

Stevie did not get back to ship the next day. She seduced him continuously, egging him on to breaking point. For two days she fed him, brought him drinks, and fucked him stupid! He left her all the money he had; 500 Kenyan Shillings (about £80). She smiled and handed it back, then kissing him, she said, "Much too little, but for you, this time, it's free!"

Stevie could not believe it. He asked, "Next time how much?"

"For you? 1,000 Shillings or $200." They kissed tenderly, saying their goodbyes, she then drove him back and dropped him off at the port gates.

Stevie was a gibbering wreck by the time he got back to the ship.

Immediately, he was hauled in front of the Captain who lectured him on the dangers of getting drunk and the risks of getting mugged in strange and dangerous countries.

It was Stevie's first time drinking shukichie,- a native delicacy and his head was in bits. All he could manage was "Yes sir! No sir! I promise I'll never do it again sir!"

The Captain logged three days' pay for failing to turn out for work, so Stevie decided to go straight to his bunk where he crashed for over 14 hours! He was shattered.It was just passed 8:30 that evening when he was awakened by a loud bang on the door.

"Go away." Stevie called out. But that made no difference. Bang, bang, bang! "Stevie." Bang, bang, bang! "Come on get up!"

"Who is it?" He managed to shout out between bangs.

"It's Matt. Hurry up and open the door."

"Who?"

"Matt." Bang, bang, bang! "Come on man, open the fucking door." He kept on banging on the door.

"Matt's not here! Now fuck off and leave me alone!"

But he persisted. Bang, bang, bang! There was no way Stevie was going to get any more sleep. He managed to climb out of his daybed and unlock the door.

In walked Matt, but he was not what caught his gaze. Following behind was what he could only describe as pure sex on legs! Standing at least 4in. taller than Stevie and wearing 6in. stiletto heels, she wore a skin tight deep blue satin halter neck dress, the hem stopping just below her knees. The tightness of her dress, along with the pointed heels gave her a very sexy wiggle as she entered his cabin.

Her skin had a deep olive glow, and her jet black hair fell in curls and folds past her waistline which looked tiny compared to the huge breasts fighting to expose themselves from the strains of the satin dress, with her nipples trying to poke through the thin fabric. Her big black eyes pulled you into them and her high gloss lipstick made her lips so moist you just lusted to kiss them. She was instant hard-on material. And an instant hard-on he got!

Not again, I said to myself. *This has happened before, and I'm not falling for it twice.*

"This is Millie, apparently you met her sister last night and she's here to invite us to dinner at their home this..." Matt started to explain but Stevie cut in. "Hold it! Just hold on a minute Matt, her sister squeezed every last drop of energy from me over two fucking days." He chuckled and said "I'm absolutely fucked! I mean just look at the state I'm in." He then turned to Millie who just stood there, staring and running her tongue over her lips.

God! I nearly came, just watching her!

Instead all he could manage was "Hello!"

"Hello." She smiled back. He almost came again.

"Tell Darlina I'm sorry, maybe another time." Stevie could see the disappointment in Matt's eyes but he managed to get them to leave. He returned to his bunk but found it impossible to fall back to sleep, and after ten minutes Stevie decided to get up, have a shower and go get something to eat.

It was 10pm when he stepped over the threshold into the mess room. Stevie noticed the television was giving off some African drum music and did not think much about it as he entered the adjacent pantry. He poured a coffee, made a cheese sandwich and re-entered the mess room. As he placed his meal on a table, he noticed someone sitting a couple of tables away watching the television and playing with the remote. Stevie assumed he was a docker as they were working 24 hours and he was taking his break, although, he wondered why a docker was taking a break in the crew mess room and did strike him as odd!

"Hello." Stevie called out. He answered with the same.

"Do you speak English?" Stevie asked, reaching over for the remote. "Little." He gestured with his thumb and forefinger.

"Are you on your break?" Stevie asked again, trying to make conversation. "You're not really allowed to have it in here."

In broken English he said, "I not workman. I business man."

"Really, what kind of business are you in?" Stevie got up and moved towards him.

"Little this...little that." He said as he stood up. He was massive, at least 7ft., but Stevie supposed that was normal. After all, he had never met a Zulu under 6ft. Anyway, he stretched out his hand and said;"My name is Jacob, and if you're interested, I have a proposition for you."

Stevie shook his hand. It was huge.

"What kind of a proposition?"

"Do you smoke grass?" He asked.

"Does a bear shit in the woods?" Stevie answered and laughed, "Or how about; do fish fuck in water?" But he noticed the look of confusion on Jacob's face and realised he could not understand a word of what he had said.

"I'm sorry," Steve apologised. "Yes!"

Jacob began skinning up. Stevie was about to have his first taste of East African Bush. After only two draws, he felt his head going numb as though a cloud was forming inside his skull. He tried to stand up and found with great difficulty that his legs were not working properly.

"Jesus, this is fucking strong shit!" he stammered. He rolled another and Stevie soon became a gibbering wreck! It was so powerful, he was almost tripping. They laughed and joked for what seemed like ages but no more was said about his proposition. Jacob promised he would return the next day and they would talk. He left a small amount for Stevie before leaving.

Stevie was almost asleep by the time he returned to his cabin and could barely remember passing out. It was his day off the following day and Matt had asked if he was going ashore. Stevie told him of his encounter the previous night and Matt decided to stay on board with him. They sat in the mess room drinking some beers and watching a local news program on TV. Time was passing by and he knew Matt was getting a bit restless as he was dying to get ashore. "Fuck!" He said, "Are you sure he's coming back tonight?"

"Yeah, I'm sure."

"Hell! You can walk down the street and pick it yourself." Matt had raised his voice and was about to say something more when a deep voice called out, "True, but then you'll need to dry it out thoroughly, and that would take several weeks." There was an eerie silence. Both Matt and Stevie turned towards the voice, then at each other and burst out laughing.

"Hello Jacob, this is Matt." They shook hands and sat down.

"Coffee?" Matt asked. "How about a whiskey?" Stevie said and went over to the bar, poured three glasses and returned to his seat.

Jacob had a plastic bag with him which he opened and showed them the contents. The aroma was over powering that Stevie was sure he was a little stoned already. There were very few leaves to speak of but loads of branches. At the end of each branch was a fat '*head*' of solid '*bub*' about 18in long. The resin was so thick Stevie was having trouble letting go. His fingers were sticking together, and he spent the next 15 minutes trying to suck them clean. He was almost as stoned as he was the previous night and he had not even smoked any yet!

Matt then took the bag through to the galley and placed the bag on the scales. It weighed a little over one kilo. Stevie poured another drink but with difficulty as he could not stop giggling. When Matt returned he asked Jacob the price for the bag. "Soap!" Was all he said.

"Soap?" Stevie asked, looking very puzzled.

"Soap!" He repeated and made a gesture as though he was washing his hands.

"You mean soap as in washing?" Matt asked. Stevie stood up and went to his cabin, took an unopened bar of Lux toilet soap and returned to the mess room. "This kind of soap?" he said holding the bar up for Jacob to see. "Yes! And ten dollars."

"How much soap for this bag?" Matt asked.

"One bar soap, plus $10 for one bag of grass."

Stevie couldn't believe his ears. He passed the soap to Jacob, who then handed the bag to Stevie. Then he shook their hands and asked if they wanted more.

"Of course." said Matt.

Well, who better to make friends with than the storekeeper! Each day, for the next three weeks, Jacob and two of his friends boarded the vessel, each carrying two plastic bags, each weighing a kilo, and each costing a bar of toilet soap. At this rate Stevie was running out of places to conceal the goods. He began stripping down the stuff and packing about half a pound into 2oz empty tobacco tins to make it easier to stow away. Scavenging around to look for places to hide the cannabis, Stevie discovered that many good hiding places had already housed other illicit goods: heroine, cocaine, diamonds, even several gold bars. It seemed like he was not the only one on board smuggling.

'I began to wonder if others, looking for hiding places, had came across my stash? I'll need to check over all my hiding places and make sure none was missing. I had often wondered about customs on arriving at foreign ports. I'd never seen a ship search, never en-countered my cabin, nor anyone's cabin, being searched. The normal procedure was that the custom officers would board the ship, head directly to the Captain's cabin, and that was the last you saw of them till they left the ship!'

Matt and Stevie kept it secret. After all, no point in letting others know, but it was not long before Willie became suspicious as they were constantly stoned. They had to let him in.

"How much is there aboard?" Willie asked taking a long draw.

"So far, 27 kilos. I think."

Coughing and spluttering as he could not hold the smoke in. "How much?" Not sure what to believe. "You got 27 kilos of grass stowed away on board? Where the fuck at?"

Stevie and Matt had managed to stow away only 8 kilos amongst the piping down below. And that space was limited. Therefore, remembering Ricky and his first job, the rest was stowed in the bilges.

"Are you stupid or what?" Piped up Willie. "We're light ship to Christmas Island. The bilges will be flooded!" "It's well waterproofed." Stevie assured him, "It'll keep dry. Trust me!"

"And what about the smell?"

"I had to order extra coffee to pack into the containers, that subdues the aroma."

"And how does someone so young know that?" Whether the grass was affecting him, but he kept up the third degree questioning.

"I had a good teacher, a bosun I sailed with for over two years, Ricky, have you heard of him?"

Matt cut in. "That wouldn't be Ricky McEwan from Glasgow? I heard he died last year."

"He did, in my arms, in a Geisha House. Injected bad shit into the back of his knees. I saw his skin turned green!"

"That must have been terrible for you." Said Willie, sympathy showing through.

"Over two years I sailed under him, and not once suspected him of using heroine. Fucked me up a bit."

"Do you have a contact in Auckland?" Questioned Willie. He must think he's a cop.

"No, but I got a couple of phone numbers in Australia. I'm hoping that'll suffice."

"I may be able to offload some in Auckland. How much do we have Stevie?"

"There's 30 kilos down the bilges, and maybe another ten in the engine room."

"OK! Leave it with me."

They sailed light ship for sixteen days. One night, about 4 am, Stevie could not sleep, so decided to visit the pantry for something to eat. His cabin was on the poop deck, the pantry and mess room were one deck below on the main deck. The staircase leading down was split in two staircases. Apart from the constant engine noise, he could hear someone sobbing. Turning round on the landing, Stevie noticed someone sitting on the bottom of the stairs. As he approached, he recognised the third engineer, Gordon, his head in his huge hands crying. An almost empty bottle of gin lay beside him, along with a small leather bag. Sitting down beside him, Stevie placed an arm around his shoulder hoping to comfort him. Gordon was a very big man, about 6ft. 5Ins. Tall, thick black hair with huge eyebrows, deep dark eyes, and sporting a large bushy beard and moustache. He weighed about 90 kilos.

"Gordon," he began shaking him. "Gordon, can you hear me?"

He slowly lifted his head from his hands, tears streaming down his face. He stared at Stevie for a couple of minutes, and blurted out, "Hey man, I'm fucking shafted!" Returning his head to his hands, the sobs became uncontrollable. Stevie was having trouble trying to calm him.

Suddenly, Gordon thrusted the small leather bag to Stevie, almost knocking over the bottle of gin, and said "Look!"

I opened the pouch and was fascinated by its contents. It contained several uncut diamonds.

'That answers my question of who belongs to the diamonds I keep finding when looking for secret hiding place.'

"What is the problem?" Stevie asked him while rubbing his shoulders.

"I can't find anywhere to hide them." His sobs got louder.

"Leave it with me, I've an idea, we'll talk about it in the morning!"

Using all the strength he could muster, Stevie managed to get him to his feet. It took over an hour to get him to his cabin, as, unfortunately for Stevie, it was three decks above us.

It was two days later when Gordon and Stevie bumped into each other again. Staring down at him with those dark, serious eyes of his, Gordon said, "I will not let another drop of gin pass my lips again. I vaguely remember talking to you, but I do know what we were talking about." Resting his hand on Stevie's shoulder, he continued, "Whatever happened, it's between you and me, can I trust that?"

His huge presence over Stevie had him nodding his head in awe!

"The cannabis you have been finding is mine. I won't say anything if you don't!"

Underneath the mass of hair round his mouth, Stevie was certain a smile appeared under it all. Gordon stuck out his hand, "Deal?"

Stevie took hold of his gigantic hand and shook it. "Deal!"

They arrived at Christmas Island to load another cargo of phosphate, only this time the full load was discharged in Auckland (New Zealand). Then, to Port Lincoln for grain. Matt made contact, and managed to sell five kilos.

"What's the going price." Stevie asked, offering Matt a beer, which he gladly took and downed it in one go.

"$400 a kilo." He said and handed over $2000.

"Take $500 each, and the remaining $500." Suggested Willie, "we can start a kitty, and split it when we sign off."

"Sounds good to me." Said Stevie. And they shook hands to confirm it.

The schedule had gone to pot as they encountered a dockers' strike in Auckland lasting 2 days. That made the ship late, missing the tide enabling them to dock at Port Lincoln, therefore, they lay anchored 7 days awaiting the next neap tide. Willie and Stevie spent the second night on the arse end with their fishing lines and a case of beer.

They caught a 2 metre long swordfish, and two reef sharks. One measured three and a half metres, the other just over four. In the morning, they strung them up and took photos, they removed their teeth, fins, and the sword from the swordfish, then threw the rest back into the sea for others to have their dinner. Besides, the stink was unbearable.

The next day the tide was high enough to dock alongside. It was late in the afternoon and some of them; Matt, Willie, and Stevie were ready to spend the night on the town. It was a small town, population about 10,000. Walking down what Stevie assumed to be the main street reminded him of an old western movie town. Eventually they arrived at the first pub. Entering through swing doors, the floor was covered in sawdust, at least Stevie thought so. There were no tables nor chairs, just a bar covering three quarters of the room. Behind the bar stood two barmen, and a bar woman. And that was it! No optics or fancy displays. No posters or adverts, absolutely nothing! Several customers turned to look as they approached the bar. The bar woman asked what they would like?

"Three beers please." Said Matt.

"Sure mate. Would that be flagons or schooners?" She asked. She was dressed like a Goth wearing a long purple velvet dress of the Gypsy type; off the shoulder and floor length. Gloves to match reaching up to her shoulders. Her thick wavy almost black hair with purple streaks hung down her back, caressing her buttocks.

She looked about 25, but it was difficult with tell all the make up. The corset of her dress was laced tight, enhancing her tiny waist and ample breast, that were struggling to break free. They looked at each other. Her deep metallic grey eyes lured you into their depths.

"Umm..." Stevie began muttering when Matt said. "What's the difference?" He could hear sniggers and tittering in the background. "Flagons!" Said Willie.

Out of nowhere three very large glasses suddenly appeared on the bar. Then she produced a hand pump and began filling them up.

Stevie soon realized a flagon was approximately a pint and a half. This was his first visit to South Australia. He was barely 17! He was underage! How could he possibly drink that much? Stevie thought one or two of the locals were suspicious and gave him funny looks, but no one said a word.

"Off the boat?" The Goth beauty said from behind the bar. Matt turned and answered, "Yeah! We're looking for the night spots."

She laughed, "This is it!" And the whole bar laughed with her.

Turning to Stevie, she smiled, saying. "You look a little young."

When she smiled, her large mouth, two perfect rows of teeth seemed to widen more. She could brighten up any dull day.

"Too young to drink? Yes!" he felt his face redden.

"I'm sorry! Would you like a juice or a coffee?" Her beautiful grey eyes transfixed him. Her heavy black eye shadow and liner enhanced them making them appear much larger.

"Black coffee no sugar please." he heard sniggering in the background.

"Just how I like my men." She teased. "And don't listen to those pricks, that's all they are, and lame ones at that.

They laughed together.

She extended her gloved hand. "My name is Sandy, what's yours?"

"Stevie." They shook hands, their eyes met and held each other for several moments.

Time was getting on and Stevie was on early watch, so Matt announced they were leaving.

Sandy called out Stevie's name and beckoned him to her. She handed him a piece of paper and said, "There's a party at that address tomorrow night. You're more than welcome Stevie, including your friends!"

"Thank you. I may take you up on that."

"Please do."

As he turned to leave, she blew him a kiss saying. "Good night!"

Stevie blew one back.

After dinner that evening, Willie, Matt and Stevie glammed themselves up and headed for the address Sandy gave.

Arriving, they entered through a non-conspicuous door and down a spiral staircase. A couple dressed in Gothic gear greeted them.

"Welcome." Said the girl. Her smile brightened up the somewhat dull surroundings. "May I take your jackets?"

"Will we get them back?" Stevie joked.

"Maybe." She laughed, "that depends if you're a good boy!"

Her male companion spoke for the first time. "So how did you know there was a party here?"

"Sandy invited us." Said Willie.

"And what sort of sexy accent is that?" The lovely punk said as she took our jackets,

"Scottish!"

"Really?" She sounded surprised. Then, "Of course, you're off the ship. Well, welcome Scottish sailors, please enter and enjoy yourselves."

They thanked her and entered. The strong smell of cannabis almost floored them.

The room was dimly lit. Loud punk music screamed from a band dancing wildly about the stage. A hoard of low tables filled most of the room which were full with Goths of all ages. One side was cleared for dancing. That was packed!

They struggled to make their way through the melee.

Also, they must have stood out like a sore thumb wearing jeans and casual shirt among the fantastic outfits worn by everyone else.

It was Sandy who spotted him first. "Stevie."

Through the din, he turned and spotted Sandy frantically waving.

"There she is." Stevie called to Willie and Matt. "Follow me."

Reaching her table, she'd already commandeered seats and it was good to sit.

"This place is mobbed." Stevie declared. "For such a small town, I've never seen so many Goths."

Sandy laughed. "They come from all over South Australia for this monthly gathering."

Her hair now had crimson highlights. She wore crimson eye make, thick, with long false eyelashes, which emphasised the greyness and depth.

"How long are you here for?" She asked.

"Three or four days." Answered Willie.

Her shiny crimson lips were truly inviting. And to top it all, she wore a crimson dress made of some shiny material, so short it barely covered her crotch. Her black fishnet stockings held up with black satin suspenders were in full view. On her feet she wore very high over the knee black platform boots.

'Wow! What a sexy woman. I'm already feeling stirrings. Behave Stevie.'

She introduced them to her friends. Three woman and two men who all seemed friendly, kept asking questions. 'Where they were from? Where they were going? What is it like to live in Scotland? And so on.

"Not drinking Stevie?" Sandy asked. "This is a private party, you can if you want!"

"So you're teasing me now eh?" He felt a little embarrassed.

"No, but try this instead." She handed over a lit joint.

Stevie took two draws and passed it to Matt.

Whether it was the accumulation of breathing in the fumes, or this was some strong shit, or maybe Stevie was not used to it, but he felt his head spinning, eyes rolling in their sockets, he began to pass out. He felt a hand tugging at him. Brought back to reality, Stevie saw a beautiful smiling face, calling.

"Stevie. Are you OK?"

"I think so. What kind of shit is this? I was almost tripping!"

"Like it?" She asked. "Very difficult to get in Port Lincoln. Only time I can get is at these monthly parties when some of my friends bring it."

"I have some on board if you're interested?"

"You're kidding?" She looked profoundly into his eyes, as if searching for truth.

"No! I'm not kidding. I have East African Bush, a lot of it!"

"How much?"

"How much do you want?"

She gave him a friendly punch on his arm "Now who's teasing who?"

"I'm serious Sandy, how many kilos do you want?"

"Wow, you're talking that much!" Once again she stared into his eyes for several moments. "Wait here, don't you dare leave. I'll be back!"

Watching her leave, those legs seem to go on forever. While she was gone, Stevie explained to Willie and Matt what they'd discussed and where she'd gone.

"Have you given her a price?" Asked Willie.

"No, I'm playing it by ear."

Time was passing and Stevie started to feel a little anxious. Then suddenly, he caught a glimpse of Sandy appearing from a door at the far end waving him over. Arriving by her side, her perfume thrilling him, she took Stevie's hand and led him through the door into what appeared to be a storeroom. There were two others in the room and Sandy introduced them.

"This is Eric and Graham. They are the ones that supply this town monthly."

They shook hands. "Hello."

"How much per kilo are you selling?" Asked Eric. His face had several piercings, one in his lip made him talk with a slight lisp.

"$500 dollars."

Stevie spotted Sandy standing away from proceedings. She was smiling and blowing him a kiss.

"Is that for each kilo, or can they negotiate discounts?"

"I can do that. How many kilos do you require?"

"20."

"I can do 3 hundred at that."

He arranged for Eric and Graham to board the ship tomorrow night.

"That'll give me time to collect funds." Graham said.

"Can I come?" Piped up Sandy. "I'll be good." She bore a wicked smile.

"Sure." Stevie said. "I look forward to it then."

He left and found Willie and Matt. Once he explained what happened, they decided to leave. They caught a taxi back to the ship and began to gather the 20 kilos required.

That proved harder than anticipated. It took until 3am before they managed to retrieve it from the bilges. By the time Stevie got to his bunk, he was out like a light.

That night, shortly after ten, a car pulled up at the gangway. Stevie was excited to see Sandy at the wheel. She got out with Eric and Graham following. It was dark, yet he could tell by the shimmering she wore a full length black PVC coat. Once on board he led them to his cabin.

"Please come in."

Stevie had spent some time cleaning as his cabin was a mess, now, it looked presentable. He took Sandy's coat, the material felt sensuous to touch.

He had never felt anything like it before, and hung it in his wardrobe. She wore a tight black PVC pencil skirt with a top and gloves to match. She also wore black thigh boots, disappearing underneath her skirt. He could only describe her as stunning!

"Sit down, make yourselves comfortable." Eric and Graham sat on his daybed, while Sandy sat at the desk chair. "Can I get you anything? Beer, or coffee?"

The men chose beers. He removed two from his fridge.

"OK to drink from the can? I've no glasses here." Stevie asked.

"I'll have a coffee." Sandy said. Then smiling sarcastically, she asked "Do you have a cup?" Stevie just smiled back.

As the night wore on, he produced a set of kitchen scales, thanks to Willie, and began weighing each parcel, then placing them into his holdall.

Once that was completed, Eric began counting out cash from a holdall he'd brought.

"That's $6,000 we agreed on," he said, returning the cash to the bag, and handing it over to Stevie.

"That's right." Stevie replied as he handed over his bag. They shook hands. There were smiles all around.

Graham asked. "Will you be back?" He stood 6ft. at least. Strong athletic body suggested he attended the gym often. Short blonde hair sporting a well-trimmed moustache and beard. No facial piercings.

"Not sure. It's a possibility every two to three months, we're under contract to transport grain to Mombasa."

As they were leaving, Sandy asked if she could return once she'd taken Eric and Graham home.

"That would be lovely, but I'm early watch."

'What was I saying? How I would love to have her back. She was such a sexy woman. She was 9 years older than

I. Was she looking for a Toy Boy? If so, I'll be her Toy Boy forever. I developed a hard on thinking about it.'

"I promise I won't keep you awake." She teased. Helping her put on her coat, she kissed Stevie on the forehead saying. "I'll be back!"

He waited for an hour on deck before she finally arrived. Sneaking her aboard was easier than he thought. As soon as he locked the cabin door, without even removing her coat, she attacked Stevie, pushing him onto the bunk and smothering him with kisses. Eventually, he managed to break free.

"For fuck sake Sandy, slow down."

Gasping she said. "I've been horny all day, please don't ask me to slow down."

"Sandy, I'm only 18." Before he could say more, she planted her beautiful lips on his forcing her tongue down his throat. Stevie almost came at once.

"I don't care how old you are, I want you!" Once more forcing her mouth on his.

Eventually coming up for air Stevie said. "You haven't taken off your coat for fuck sake!"

She wasn't listening. Swirling her tongue around inside his ear she whispered. "Fuck me! Fuck me!" Over and over again.

That was the limit. He almost ripped her coat from her back and began to find a way of removing her dress, which he found, took great difficulty. She was tugging at his jeans zip. She kept her promise of not keeping him awake as Stevie grew limp inside her and fell asleep.

He woke at 7 with the usual alarm call from the Bridge. Opening his eyes, Stevie was shocked to discover he was alone. A note on his desk read:

"Good morning Stevie. Thanks for a lovely evening, sorry I couldn't make your breakfast. Maybe next time. Love Sandy."

'I was shocked and fell back on my bunk. We were sailing
for Mombasa tomorrow. Will I see her again? I hope so.
She was a one in a million woman!'

Every day, coaches of sightseers, or school children would stop quayside and looked in wonder at the vast ship loading grain. They became very popular.

On the day they sailed, almost the entire town was waving goodbye from the dockside. There was even a coach load of nuns came to bid them farewell.

No sign of Sandy. Stevie felt a little disappointed.

As the last mooring ropes were released, and three tugs began manoeuvring the ship away from her berth, several of the crew including Stevie stood on bollards along the stern. Gerald, the third officer gave the signal and they all dropped their trousers, bent over, put their heads between their knees, and kissed their asses goodbye! The term was known as *'spreaders'*.

Those waving them off were met with that shocking vision they may remember for the rest of their lives.

For their part, they were each taken up in front of the Skipper and logged two days' pay. It took almost 6 days sailing before Stevie got Sandy out of his mind. Another two weeks till they reached Kenya. Stevie took the opportunity to check his hiding places. Getting rid of 20 kilo left him wondering how much remained.

The money was shared equally between Willie, Matt and Stevie. This was their third trip and crew members were due to reliefs.

"Are you going home Stevie?" Asked Matt one night while chilling over a joint and a couple of beers.

"Not if I can help it."

"I don't blame you. That was some chick you were with."

"Yea. She's my contact." He lit another joint. "What are you gonna do?"

"I don't have a choice. There are issues at home that I need to sort."

A knock on the door disturbed their thoughts.

"Come in!" It was Willie. Stevie handed the joint to him. "Beer in the fridge if you want."

"Just the smoke. Thanks."

"We were just discussing whether to sign off. What about you?"

"I'd love to stay. That's a good deal we got going here." He drew on the joint and passed it to Matt.

"So why break it up?" Stevie asked.

"Hey! You go ahead, but I've a young family waiting back home. I'm sure you understand!"

'I didn't really. How could I? So they were deserting me and I need to do this alone. So be it!'

They divided the accumulating cash; $2250 each to Willie and Ricky. A tidy sum to take home, which left Stevie with $2000. They were all happy. A good voyage all round.

Two days before docking, the Chief Stewart came round asking who wanted relieved. Stevie refused. Nothing more was said.

Darlina was waiting shoreside, but he had to tell her he was working night shift. She looked stunning and so she should. After all, she was a premium prostitute charging $200 dollars per day.

'When I thought about it, every foreign woman I've met so far have been whores (except Sandy). They were the best for teaching you about sex I must admit! Darlina and I

saw each other twice a week each trip. Besides, I couldn't afford any more!'

Stevie was working alone now. It would take a while to suss out the new crew members. Thankfully, they were berthed 5 days before they arrived, by which time Jacob and Co had brought over 30 kilos. Willie and Matt helped stow it away. Stevie had then to explain to Jacob not to bring more.

"But only for the rest of this trip." He managed to make Jacob understand. "Different people now, but next trip, I will see you, OK?"

"OK!"

The two week voyage to Christmas Island was fraught with problems. Generators kept playing up due to excessive vibrations from the prop. The weather was notorious. With the ship unladen and rough seas, Stevie was thankful when Christmas Island appeared on the horizon.

Once laden, ports of discharge were Wollongong, Sydney (New South Wales) and Melbourne (Victoria). Then on, once again to Port Lincoln for grain.

Stevie got friendly with Basher, one of the new greasers. Short fair hair donning a thin moustache well trimmed. He guessed he was about 20, heavy built as he attended the gym often. If Basher was taller than his 5ft 7ins, he wouldn't look so plump. He had a brilliant sense of humour and was always up for a laugh. Like Stevie, he also took a toke.

They spent a night drinking in Sydney and Melbourne, where Stevie decided to let him in on his secret.

"You've got 30 kilos of shit on this boat?" He looked shocked. "Tell me you're fucking kidding?"

"No! And have I told the right person?"

He was silent for several minutes. "I've never seen that much grass. Where is it?"

"Hidden."

"OK. But where?"

"Everywhere! And I need you to help retrieve it before we reach Port Lincoln. Can I trust you?"

"Sure Stevie."

He was true to his word.

The last night in Melbourne was spent gathering as much grass as possible, weighing and packing it into kilos.

"Only 23 kilos I count." Said Basher, "want to go look for more?"

"We can't."

"Why not? There's still time."

"I've forgotten where it is." Stevie sniggered. "No worries, we'll get it next time."

"I guess your contact knows you're coming?"

"I hope so." Almost at a whisper. Thoughts began filling Stevie's head of the last time he saw her, and he remembered the hurt he felt at not seeing her again when they sailed.

Tying up, his eyes scoured the dock side. There was no sign of her. After lunch, both Basher and Stevie went ashore. They went to the pub where Stevie first met her. Now he's nearly old enough to drink, Stevie ordered two flagons.

"Is Sandy not working?" he asked the barman who was serving them.

"She only works 3 evenings a week mate." He noticed Stevie's disappointment and said, "You should try her boutique."

Stevie perked up. "She owns a boutique? I didn't know that!"

"A couple hundred yards down the main street. Can't miss it. She does all that punk stuff. I just can't come to grips with the young 'uns these days."

Perfect! Then to Basher. "Wait here, she might not like strange company. I'll be back soonest."

The shop was easy to find. The pavement outside was packed with clothing rails and loads of accessories. Above the door in big black Gothic writing read 'Sandys Boutique'.

Stevie felt a little apprehensive walking through the entrance. There were several customers, 8 in all, looking through the wonderful outfits. No sign of Sandy. Behind the counter sat a female with very short pink hair reading a magazine. As he approached she looked up and got to her feet. Her eyes, thick with pink and black make up enhancing the deep brown pupils. Her smile stretched from ear to ear was warm and inviting. She wore a short pink leather dress, black fishnets and very high pink knee boots.

"Hi! Can I help you?"

"Hi! Yes, I'm looking for Sandy." Stevie began to feel a little nervous.

"Ah, you've just missed her. Her husband called to take her to lunch."

His heart collapsed.

'Why am I not surprised? I should have known. Certain things didn't add up. She never spoke of her family, nor where she lived, and when I asked, she averted the question, or changed the subject. The only woman I've met who's not a whore, is married! Fucking wonderful.'

"Would you like to wait, she won't be too long." Her warm smile could not lift his spirits.

"No thanks!" he turned to leave, saying. "Just tell her Stevie was here."

"Stevie? The Scottish sailor?"

"Yes."

"Wait a minute. She left you a message." And opening a drawer, she handed Stevie an envelope.

"Thanks." He took the envelope, said good bye and left.

Back at the pub, Basher looked bored. "Thank fuck you're back, this place is shit."

"Well let's go."

Back on board Stevie explained to Basher the contents of the letter. "So we're expecting a visit tonight?"

"Yes. But I'll need to ask you not to attend."

Eric and Graham arrived at midnight. The procedure went like clockwork. Kilos weighed and packaged. Money counted and handed over. One hitch was they were expecting 20 kilos, but managed to produce the extra $3300.

"Next time." Eric explained. "Let Sandy know the amount so we bring enough cash."

"OK, but that may be difficult." Then he added. "When did she get married?"

"Last month, she'd timed it for the gathering. Brilliant wedding."

Stevie said little, and when they were gone. Basher entered his cabin. "Everything OK?"

"Fine." Stevie counted out $1,450 and handed it to him. "Not bad for fuck all don't you think?"

"I've never seen so much cash. This is fantastic!"

"Is everything OK Stevie, you look down. We should be celebrating!"

"Just shattered, that's all. Time for bed!"

"See you tomorrow then. Goodnight!"

"Goodnight!"

Another six months passed when Stevie was asked if he wanted to go home, he refused. He was making a fortune and he had just turned 18, and he had just delivered his very own first ton of East African bush to Australia. Each time they docked in Port Lincoln, Eric and Graham would be there, and business sorted and paid. There was no sign of Sandy.

'I felt she was avoiding me. Would I see her again? I hope so. Her memory will go on. She was the first woman I had feelings for. And the first and only woman to rape me for love. Why she took me that night when she already had a fellow confused me. Was it a last fling before marrying? Was I the first prick available? Maybe? I'll never know!'

Each time they docked in Mombasa, Darlina would pick Stevie up and take him to her home. Another 3 round trips and 6 months later, instead of being asked, he was ordered to leave by a new Skipper who had joined 6 months prior.

"But I have nothing at home. Why would I want to go there?"

"Well, you've managed to stay on this ship for 18 months. You're only supposed to do 6!"

"Has anyone complained about my work Sir?" he asked, desperate to stay. "No no. No complaint there! It's just that I've noticed you walking down the aisles sideways. And you seem to have a twitch in one of your eyes."

"Do I?" Stevie was shocked.

"Yes! You do! No arguments, you're going home!"

'Damn! What am I gonna tell both Jacob and Darlina? And how the fuck am I gonna let Eric and Graham know? And what about Sandy?'

Docking around 8pm, Stevie noticed the relief crew were already unloading from a coach keyside. Parked in front was Darlina. Stevie thought it was best that he did not see her. Once his work was done, he headed straight to his cabin. His two suitcases were already packed, one with cash, the other with cannabis. (No need for anything else). All members who were relieved then proceeded down the gangway and onto the coach. Darlina saw him and got out of her car and approached him with a worrying expression.

"Where are you going?"

"I'm sorry, I've been ordered home, I have to go." Stevie tried to kiss her as tears filled her eyes but he was forced onto the coach.

'That was the end of a wonderful sexy relationship I will never forget. She taught me much. She treated me as her toy-boy and I loved it!'

They were taken straight to the airport and boarded a small twin prop air plane. All the seats were full of people or caged animals. There were also two Matt goats and four pigs. They were crammed in like sardines. The engines coughed and spluttered as they started.

'Fuck, is this thing gonna take off? I've never liked flying, but this plane was putting the shits in me. I wanted to get off. I felt sick and paranoid and scared.'

Stevie's worries subsided when they landed an hour later in Nairobi. From there, they were driven to the Oscar Hotel for the night. Their flight to Heathrow was due at 5am and they were told not to miss it.

"Fancy a drink?" Stevie asked Willie, "I know it's an early flight but a couple won't harm."

"Sorry Stevie, but I'm shattered. Gonna have an early night."

"OK, no problem, see you tomorrow. Goodnight!"

Because he had left his clothes on board, Stevie thought he would go and buy some new ones. So, grabbing a handful of cash, he left the hotel. He was immediately accosted by several tradesmen selling their wares and Stevie found one which suited him. He purchased denims, a flowery shirt and a leather jacket which he changed into straight away. He gave the seller the hotel's address. He said he would have Stevie's old clothes taken there. Stevie thanked him and headed for the first boozer. It was a good one as there were no bar girls for which he was grateful as that was the last thing he needed.

The first thing he needed was a drink. He ordered beer and a whiskey chaser, collected them and found a nice secluded seat. He needed to think!

'I left the UK 18 months ago and the only place I could return to was my Mam's house. That may be complicated.'

As the night went on, he was becoming slightly pissed. The bar began to get busier. Bar girls began to appear and it wasn't long before he had company. He tried hard to discourage them, and eventually he became fully pissed. And that has always been his downfall.

The next thing he remembered was being awakened by a female voice. "Stevie, I have to go." He felt a kiss on his forehead and by the time he opened his eyes, she had gone.

Puzzling, Stevie looked at his watch. It was 10:30 am!

'Aw fuck, I've missed my flight. Aw fucking damn!' But on the other hand, am I really in a hurry to get home. Do I really WANT to go home? Well, whatever, I really need to get up. I'd love to know with whom I spent the night with. (Or maybe not?)'

Dressing quickly, he went down to reception and signed out. He asked the receptionist who it was that had just left his room, and was delighted to learn it was a female.

'Phew. I'll never forget Singapore!'

Out into the bright morning sunshine, it suddenly dawned on him that he had no clue as to his whereabouts. He had slept in a strange hotel. Not the one they signed into on arrival. And for the love of him, he could not recall the name of that hotel. Everything he owned was in that hotel. He checked his pockets, still plenty of cash, and, to his utter glee, a receipt from the street seller. He was so relieved to find an address on it.

"That's a start," He said to himself and flagged down the first taxi in view.

Showing the driver the receipt Stevie asked, "Can you take me there?"

He studied it for several moments before answering. "Sure OK!"

And within minutes he pulled up at the kerb.

"How much?" Stevie asked as he climbed out of the cab.

"10 dollars."

Stevie gave the driver a $20 note, he thanked him before speeding off.

"Hey, what about my change?" Too late, suckered again!

Now he had his bearings, he walked for less than 5 minutes before he arrived at the original hotel

Of course, The Oscar, who would have forgotten that?

Anyway, on entering the lobby his name was called and a smartly dressed female approached him.

"Mr Stevie Bates?" She asked in perfect English.

"Yes. And you are?"

"My name is Malena, I work for the British Consulate." Her tone seemed harsh.

"Where have you been? You were supposed to catch a flight this morning, and I have been left here to wait."

"Hold on just a minute. I'm sorry you've had to spend your morning waiting for me but I'm still trying to get my head together. I know it's self inflicted but my head is throbbing. Why don't we go for a coffee and discuss things there?"

"I will not!" Her voice sounded very stern.

"OK! OK, please don't shout at me, I apologise. Let's at least sit down and we can start again."

I held out my hand. "Hello, My name..."

"Mr Bates, I haven't the time for this." She opened her bag and handed him an envelope. "Inside is your flight ticket, which I managed to transfer with great difficulty, onto a flight to Heathrow at 5 this afternoon. And for your sake Mr. Bates, make sure you're on it!"

With that, she stormed off without so much as a goodbye!

Looking at his watch, now 12 noon, Stevie asked the reception what time he needed to check out.

"What time is your flight?"

"5pm."

The nice chap looked through some papers, then, "We don't need your room till later. You'll need to be out by four pm."

"Will you call me at three?" Stevie asked.

"No problem." He said handing over the door key, "pleasant dreams."

Stevie went upstairs, checked his suitcases, (thank fuck they were still there, and intact) and crashed out!

The phone ringing brought him awake. His alarm call, or so he thought as he scrambled to answer.

"Mr Bates, this is Malena from the Consulate, just to make sure you get your flight."

"Well what if I do, we can alw..." She cut him off! Bitch! He thought.

Forty-five minutes later he arrived at the airport. One hour to wait and he was becoming very agitated.

'Hope I get through customs," I thought. My mind ran in overdrive, what if I get caught? Fuck, haven't thought this

out properly. I'd managed to hide the strong grass aroma
by empting 6 jars of coffee inside that case. The other case
contained cash. What's my excuse? Fuck, fuck, fuck! Calm
down Stevie, go get a drink – Good idea!'

Stevie drank whisky, not too much, but just enough to help him put on a show. He waited till the last possible moment. And, with a suitcase in each hand, British Seaman Card between my teeth, and a slight hurried stagger, he approached the check-in desk.

The customs officer was a big fat man. He was clean shaven and he wore his hair in a huge Afro style. He watched Stevie keenly as he reached the desk. Gesturing, by moving his head like a chicken, the officer took the hint and removed the card from Stevie's mouth.

"Hope I'm not late," Stevie blurted out with a slur, "I've run like hell…, see that fucking taxi driver, well I thoug…!"

He cut in, "Whoa! Slow down, You've still got a couple of minutes."

"It's just that I missed my flight this morning, and that Consulate bitch gave me a hard time, and if I miss this…"

He stamped the card with a huge grin on his face, shoved it back between Stevie's teeth and laughed. "Go, go hurry up or you will miss it again!"

'Well, that was the easy part. 5 hours to Heathrow, I'll need to
prepare myself for act 2.

Finding his seat and strapping in, relief set in quickly. Stevie soon fell asleep.

It felt like minutes later when someone nudged him. Opening his eyes he was confronted with a lovely smiling face.

"Are you awake, Mr Bates? We'll be serving meals in 15 minutes, can I get you something?"

Easing himself upright, he answered with a question.

"How long before we land?"

She looked at her watch. "About an hour."

"In that case, I'll have a treble whiskey with ice."

"Fine, but you'll need to eat something. I can't serve drink alone."

"OK. If it makes you happy, I'll have a cheese sandwich."

Her smile broadened as she went away to get the sandwich.

Landing at Heathrow was a huge shock! Stevie's plans were in jeopardy. By the time he walked down the gangway, his knees were banging together with the cold which rapidly sobered him up. He had to keep up the drunken seaman act.

For the past 18 months or so, he had been living in temperatures averaging 30 plus degrees centigrade. Sitting in the baggage claim, Stevie realised he was wearing only a t-shirt, a pair of shorts, and mere flip flops on his feet. He had gotten rid of all his clothes and other belongings to fill his suitcases with cash and cannabis. His intention was to buy a full wardrobe of new clothes when he got home. Barely able to lift the cases, Stevie joined the queue for passport control.

Creeping forward in the queue, until only a couple left in front, Stevie began involving those around him in his plan. Laughing and telling jokes to the couple in front of him. The family directly behind him had three children who were laughing at his antics. Stevie asked the youngest if he would take his red seaman's card from his back pocket and put it in his mouth. The boy giggled and obliged. Stevie kept up with the scheme until he heard; "Next".

Facing a very tall and skinny customs officer, whose long thin face showed no sign of emotion, Stevie indicated for him to remove the card from his mouth. Stevie mumbled in the best drunken slur he could muster, and asked "Would you return my card to my mouth please?"

The officer opened and studied the contents. Then looking hard at Stevie, he said, "British Seaman eh?" Stevie nodded in anticipation.

"How long are you here for?"

"I've 2 months' leave." Stevie said and thought he had just answer his question straight, but the officer looked unimpressed! Looking again at the photo, then back at Stevie, he asked "Anything to declare?"

"Yeah, I've got 6 dirty books and an ounce of dope!"

"I heard you joking earlier."

He stamped Stevie's card saying; "Get out of here!"

Stevie quickly sped out the terminal and into the first taxi. "Take me home James!"

"Funny!" The taxi driver was not amused.

"Sorry mate," Stevie tried not to laugh. He was on such a high he was not going to let the miserable driver to dampen his spirits. He calmly said, "Euston railway station please!"

'The buzz I got was amazing. How I got away with it, I believe, was pure luck! The depressive taxi driver just lost a large tip!'

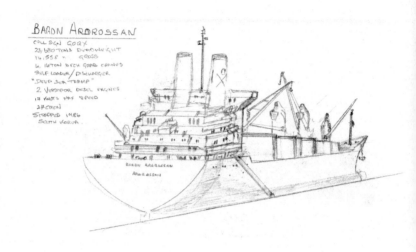

BARON ARDROSSAN

CALL SIGN GQZX
23,680 TONS DEADWEIGHT
16,558 " GROSS
4, 16 TON DECK GRAB CRANES
SELF LOADER / DISCHARGER
"DEEP SEA TRAMP"
2, VERSADOR DIESEL ENGINES
17 KNOTS MAX SPEED
27 CREW
SCRAPPED 1986
SOUTH KOREA.

BARON ARDROSSAN
ARDROSSAN

Chapter Five

M.V. Baron Ardrossan

Once he got home, Stevie had to stash his wares to prevent any of his family discovering his true life at sea. The usual arguments and debates with his Mum continued. He had grown up very quickly, and his adolescence arguments with Mum were few and far between. He pitied those who endured adolescence every day for many years.

One morning, he received a call from Hamish.

"Hey, how are you doing?" His broad Glaswegian accent prominent.

"A bit bored. What about you?"

"I'm good. Do you fancy a trip up here, I'll show you the sights of Glasgow?"

"Brilliant idea," he said. "I've never been to Glasgow, where would I stay?"

"My place, I've a spare room."

"How soon do you want me?" That did not sound right!

"Anytime Stevie, the room's ready."

He jumped at the chance to leave home. "I can check the train timetable tomorrow?"

"Perfect, just let me know your time of arrival, I'll meet you at Central Station."

They met as arranged and Hamish drove them to Shettleston, out in the east end. After a hearty dinner of "stovies" which was his first taste of Scottish cuisine, Hamish informed Stevie that he was due to meet his girlfriend, Harriot Tweedle. He thought Hamish was taking the piss, but Harriot Tweedle was indeed her real name. He then bluntly informed Stevie that Harriot's friend, Ann Thompson would be accompanying her.

"What? Are you asking me to go on a blind date?" He sounded shocked!

"She's very attractive Stevie, you'll like her."

"That may be so Hamish, but it's still a blind date, she might not like me!"

"She will, she's seen a photo of you, and she's up for it"

"What photo?" He was getting worried now.

"Remember the one we got taken in Amsterdam with Willie?" He opened a draw in his sideboard and produced the photo in question.

"And here's one of her with Harriot."

True enough, very attractive, thick wavy shoulder length auburn hair. Sexy green eyes set wide apart that hypnotised you. Full sensual lips that looked so inviting. She reminded Stevie a little of Sandy, different colour eyes, her hair was shorter, nevertheless, there was a close resemblance.

"Okay!" he said, "You invited me here to show me the lights of Glasgow, we may as well have company."

The company turned out to be perfect. An excellent sound from a local band named "Stone the Crows" playing live in a nearby pub drew them in. They had a meal there, which took a couple of hours. Then a few hours at the dancing floor and the rest of the night were spent in each other's arms.

Stevie spent the next week in Glasgow. He saw Ann nearly every day. He would have stayed in Glasgow longer, and after watching the "Walk" on the 12th of July, he fell in love with both the city and the people.

When he received a telegram from head office informing him that his flight to Vancouver was on the following day, leaving from Prestwick Airport, both Stevie and Ann felt a little sadness. Arrangements had been made and he would pick up his ticket at the Air Canada Desk. Showing her the telegram, Stevie smiled and said, "Read this part Ann, it says the trip is estimated to take three months." He was hoping to cheer her up. "That's not much time, it will fly by.....Trust me!"

"May I come and wave you off?" he heard sniffles, "Or should I say. Bon voyage?" A slight giggle, then a smile seemed to lighten up the mood. At the airport, they embraced for several minutes as his flight was announced for boarding.

The boat he flew out to Vancouver to join was named the 'Baron Ardrossan', a 24,500 tonne bulk carrier. It was built in Hahgesund Norway, launched in 1972, and named after the small fishing village on the west coast of Scotland where the company was founded in the 20's by a native called Harry Hogarth.

Stevie had problems pronouncing the name. She was the first of a new class of "Deep-Sea Tramps" and had five hatches, each the size of a baseball pitch, fed by four 25 tonne grab cranes. She could carry anything except oil and go anywhere. She could load and unload herself!. Her 5-deck superstructure resembled a luxury hotel. Each crew member had their own en-suite cabin. There was a cinema, gym, games room, and a swimming pool. She had completed her maiden voyage but was beset with engine problems. She had been fitted with two experimental engines, made from a new kind of alloy metal that was too light, so when she was unladen, the vibration from the twin props caused the cylinder heads to explode repeatedly. She was scheduled to load sulphur for several ports in Australia, then zinc concentrates for Avonmouth, and on to Rotterdam for new engines.

Stevie met Willie (chief cook) on the flight over, a wee Scotsman around 55 years old. Two small grey ruffs of hair above each ear was the only hair he possessed. A natural comic, he had Stevie in stitches within ten minutes of meeting.

A very funny character, he was sure they were going to get along. On arriving at Vancouver airport, they were met by the ship's agent, and were surprised to find another 10 crew members ranging from galley boy to chief engineer also on the flight.

"I'm afraid to say the boat's not here." Said the agent. Tuts and gasps could be heard. "There are problems with her engines apparently" He continued. A crew member stepped forward; "Hello! My name is Davy, I'm the relief 3rd Officer. Do you know where she is?" Standing at least 6ft.4in, a full mop of blond curly hair, large deep blue eyes set wide apart, a long thick nose and perfectly chiselled jaw made him look very handsome. His physique, strong and muscular meant he was a keep fit freak. Not that Stevie was into handsome men, but he wished he had Davy's height and looks.

"They have put her in dry dock at Seattle! Apparently, a few essential repairs are needed done, we're hoping she'll be here tomorrow. In the meantime I've booked rooms at the Sheridan Landmark Hotel. Get all your gear together, there's a coach waiting outside to take us there."

The hotel was very impressive. 44 stories with a 360 degree revolving restaurant at the top. The hotel was so new, only 50% was open. They all had single rooms on the 23 floor. On checking in, Stevie noticed how extremely sexy the receptionist was, he tried to catch her eye, but she was busy! As she gave him his key, Stevie asked for her name.

"Amy, and yours?" The broad welcoming smile almost floored him.

"Stevie." Always quick to capture a situation he quickly asked, "what time do you finish?"

She just smiled, so sweetly, he almost melted. She was so beautiful! Dark wavy hair falling past her shoulders. Stunning wide green eyes set above high cheek bones. A short turned-up nose and large pouting shiny red lips. Her broad smile looked delicious and friendly. Just his type! Her immaculate uniform gave her an air of authority, beauty, and sexiness all at once. As she was about to answer his question, the phone rang. Stevie's name was called so he had to leave. She caught his eye and smiled.

"I'll see you later." He said to himself. "You've no chance." Willie laughed, "She's well out of your league."

"Really? Just watch this space!"

When everyone got settled in, and spent a little time to get to know each other, Davy, our new third Officer, suggested a night in the town would help us to bond.

"After all," He said, "a happy crew maketh a happy ship." Stevie agreed with him. "Have you been here before? I've visited Victoria on Vancouver Island once, and New Westminster twice, only twenty five miles away, but never stepped foot in Vancouver City. I was looking forward to the experience, especially to get to know Amy." Stevie said.

"I've been here several times." Davy said, "I know of a couple of pubs where they have a live band every night, one in particular; Oil Can Harry's, was fantastic. I'm sure it's just the same."

"How long ago were you here?"

"Two months."

"Well, what are we waiting for? Let's go!" Only Willie and Davy began to move, the others were too shattered, suffering from a slight jet lag, gave their excuses. So, the three of them left.

'Although I'd confessed earlier that I enjoyed a toke of cannabis now and again;(mostly now than again). Davy wouldn't stop going on and on about acid. (LSD).'

"I'm not too sure." Stevie thought to himself. He had never come across the drug, never tried it.

"You'll love it." Davy said. "It can be very dangerous if you do it yourself." He began explaining the ups and downs of 'tripping'. Stevie still wasn't convinced. He knew his limits with cannabis and he could control his intake therefore his level of 'stoniness.' But acid; that was another level. After the death of Ricky, Stevie swore to himself he would take nothing but cannabis.

Davy had a bit of flair about him. He possessed the gift of the gab, a bit of a comic. Stevie liked his attitude. He was in his early 20's, successful and possessed the ability to move positively, think quickly and decisively. He stood around 5ft.11in. with short blond hair and a Van Dyke beard which suited him well and gave him a look of intelligence.

"Do you know where you're going?" Stevie asked Davy as they followed him into the city centre. "I assume you've been here before?"

"I have several times. What about you two?"

"The timber wharfs in New Westminster I have visited twice before." Stevie announced, remembering the Baron Forbes. "Also Victoria, on Vancouver Island." He also remembered Ricky and Nora, and wondered if she was still here. During a domestic incident at home, Stevie lost many of his old contact names and numbers. With Ricky gone, his chances of completing his smuggling apprenticeship were very thin. Pity! He only had another year to study. "This is my first time to Vancouver City."

"Only once before," said Willie, "that was last year. Where are you taking us Davy?"

"We're going to an area known as Gass Town," About a ten minute walk later, they entered Oil Can Harry's. Several doors led off the hallway, they followed Davy through the one on his right. The first thing that hit Stevie was the smell of cannabis, and by the time he reached the bar he felt a little light headed!

The lounge was huge and almost packed to the gunwales with party goers. To the left, a large dance floor was almost full, dancing to a live country-rock band who deafened all those near them, yet the female singers' voice was captivating. The centre was taken up by a large square bar with a 4 deep queue waiting to be served. They managed to squeeze their way through the mass of bodies and shouted their order over the din for three beers.

A huge hippie fellow stood next to Stevie, making him look like a dwarf. The hippie looked down to Stevie and blurted out in a very loud voice, "Where the hell did you get an accent like that? Ha ha ha! You sound like my dear 'ol Gran. Ha ha ha!"

As Stevie began to wipe himself from the shower that sprayed from his broad mouth, Willie said "Scotland!"

"Scotland?" He shrieked, "I thought that, my Gran comes from Scotland, Dumfries, do you know it?" Before any of us could answer, he said "Let me get you jocks a beer, oh! I see you have one, good, follow me. I'll get you all a seat." They looked at each other, pulled funny faces. "Why not," said Davy, "It's a seat!" He was a big man, at least 6ft. 4ins. almost as wide as he was tall. He had no problem pushing through the mob of dancers and party goers. He was in his mid thirty's, a huge black beard covered most of his face and his hair, tied in a pony tail hung halfway down his back.

There were several people sitting at a table when they arrived. The 'Big Man' managed to squeeze two more chairs in as those sitting made space. He then introduced himself as Bob along with the present sitting companies, whose names Stevie would never remember. They did the same and shook hands. The atmosphere was certainly party-like. He kept asking questions about Scotland, and they did their best to accommodate with answers. They never bought another drink that night.

After a long time, Stevie said to Willie, "Don't know how much more of this I can take?"

"Yeah, I agree, trouble is Davy's trying to score some acid, and I'm stoned!"

Stevie laughed, "Me too, fancy halving mine? I could use a nice score of grass."

They knew they could not be late as they were flying to Seattle in the morning. No one was sure how long the ship was to stay there, so it made economical sense. Stevie guessed it would be far cheaper doing that than staying in the Sheridan Landmark.

Just then Davy and Bob returned. "Listen guys," Davy whispered, "I've managed to get some blotto, but I'm short, do you fancy splitting it?"

"What's blotto?" Stevie asked.

"Later! How much money do you have?"

"We haven't officially started work yet, I've only about $20."

"Me also, maybe $35." announced Willie.

"Fantastic, give it me." And before they could say anything, Davy took what they had and was gone. Like Willie, Stevie had met Davy for the first time at Prestwick that morning, and he had just given the 3rd officer every penny Stevie had in his possession! Davy returned a few minutes later.

"Here," he said, handing over what seemed like a small piece of blotting paper, about 2mm square. "Place that under your tongue and leave it there while it slowly dissolves."

Once again, Willie and Stevie did as they were told, after all, he was the third officer, and Stevie's future boss. Several minutes later, Stevie recalled picking up his pint, placing it to his lips, and was about to take a drink when something caught his eye. Stevie turned his head from left to right and all he could make out was a blur of colours as if he was on a round-about. He could not recall drinking any of his pint, just these amazing colours flashing past his eyes. Stevie was brought out of this dream-like state by Davy shouting, "OK, let's go!"

The next thing Stevie remembered, he was with the others on the pavement outside the main door. He could remember all these people wishing them luck, good fortune, and "why do you have to leave?" and "Please stay!" Everyone wanted to hug and kiss them!

They decided to get a taxi, so they asked the strangers around them for directions to the nearest taxi rank, then proceeded in the direction indicated. After what seemed like hours of walking with no sign of a taxi, let alone a taxi rank, Stevie was finding difficulty in speaking. He moved, with face down watching the pavement. He lifted one foot, carried it forward several yards, left the foot there, then went back to lift his other foot and bring it along till both feet were together! "What the fuck is this shit?" he managed to call out.

Next thing he remembered was getting out of a taxi at the hotel.

After getting help to climb the steps, Stevie faced another difficult challenge to get through the hotel's huge revolving doors. He tripped, and fell head first into the revolving doors. He was spun round and round several times before being flung into the hotel reception. By now his balance had completely gone and he landed face down on the plush foyer carpet. The thick, dense thread began to grow, taller and taller around him until Stevie was convinced he was in a jungle. He began to crawl forward, pressing down on the undergrowth to make a path. He encountered several snakes, and a wild boar ran past him, almost stabbing him with its large horn. There were all sorts of weird beasties scurrying about. He also came across an elephant, a couple of monkeys and a hippopotamus. Then suddenly he felt a thud on his head and realized he had slammed head first into a tree trunk!

"Oouchhh" Stevie screamed and began to climb the trunk. As he began to stand up, he could hear a distant voice calling; "Hello! Hello! Are you still there?" It was getting louder and louder as he climbed higher and higher. When he appeared over the tree top, his heart sunk. He realized he had crawled from the swinging doors, and banged into the reception desk.

Facing him was the girl of his dream, mouth fully agape, one hand holding a phone six inches from her ear, shouting; "Hello, can you hear me?" and with the other hand, she placed his room key in his mouth. Stevie nodded his head in a gesture of thanking her, then sank back down onto the carpet. There were at least 20 to 30 people around as you would expect in such a large luxury hotel witnessing his debacle. Stevie felt so embarrassed as he pulled himself up from the lush carpet.

By this time, he did not know whether it was New York or whether it was New Year, nor where he was. By now Willie and Davy had got a hold of him and began dragging him towards the lifts.

"Hey Man," Stevie managed to say to Davy, "What the fuck is this shit?" He could not recall much over the next 24 hours but he remembered the three of them in a lift heading up to the revolving restaurant. Ordering a breakfast of steak and eggs was a mistake!

When the waitress placed the plate in front of him, Stevie stared at it for several minutes. The steak was huge, and buried beneath a mountain of onion rings, salad, mushrooms, and French fries. It was 9 am now, the restaurant was busy. A large group of people sat at the table next to them.

"I could never eat all this!" he declared.

"Just eat." Willie laughed.

One of the diners at the next table approached them and asked where they came from.

"Scotland!" Davy answered.

"I thought I recognised the accent." He held out his hand. "My name is Willie, Willie Nelson."

Davy, Willie, (their Willie), and Stevie ate breakfast in the company of American musician, Willie Nelson, his wife and his band. They were also guests and were playing that evening at 'Oil-Can Harry's'. He offered them tickets but they had to decline as they were leaving that evening.

* * *

It was a short flight to Seattle, yet he remembered very little. Stevie was having flash backs at everything he concentrated his eyes upon. They were picked up at the airport and taken directly to the docks where the ship had just been taken out of dry dock within the last 30 minutes. She had sailed, unladen from Japan, which had taken almost 21 days. That had caused several of her cylinder heads to blow repeatedly. She was capable of 19 knots with both engines operating. Now, she was lucky to do 12.

Once the formalities of relieving crew members were over, and each of them got settled into their cabins, it was dinner time. Afterwards, Davy invited both Willie and Stevie to his cabin for a 'nightcap' as he put it.

"What the fuck did you give us?" Stevie asked Davy, entering his cabin. Willie was already there. "I think I'm still buzzing. I can't think straight, especially when I want to speak."

"I told you." Davy laughed, "Blotto!"

"OK! But what the fuck is blotto? I mean I've moved stuff all over the world, but I've never heard of blotto!"

"Here! I'll show you!"

From under his daybed, he produced a fairly large and bulky package."This is what your dollars got you." He opened the envelope and took several sheets of A4 size blotting paper from it. Each sheet was symmetrically perforated into small 2mm squares. (about 5000 per sheet). Then, using a syringe, the blotting paper is soaked with liquid LSD. Willie and Stevie looked at the sheets laid out on the bunk, then looked at each other, then at Davy.

"I think it's the first time Stevie has taken acid" said Willie. "This is my third time, but I've never had anything as strong as that." He looked at Stevie saying, "I'm still buzzing also!"

"Wait till I tell you what just happened prior to coming here." Stevie said, "I was sitting on my daybed staring up in one corner, when suddenly, my eyes erupted from my eye sockets and shot up to the far away top corner of my cabin, they turned round and began staring down at me! Can you believe that? I thought I was really going to freak out. Then, while staring at myself, my head split from front to back, I thought I was going to freak out, but, from my head emerged balloons and shapes of all sizes and colours you could never have imagined."

"Awesome!" Said Willie, "That could have gone really bad though. I've never tripped as heavy as that."

"This stuff is the Prima Donna." Davy held up a sheet. "This contains at least 5000 individual tabs. We have ten sheets, that's 50,000 tabs of LSD which we paid $65 for. Each tiny tab at today's prices, is $10."

"Is that what you and Bob were up to?" Stevie asked.

"Yeah! I didn't believe it myself at first, I thought he was kidding."

"So we're rich?" Asked Willie. "Well, until we can sell it." Turning to Davy, he asked. "Have you any contacts in Australia?"

"I've checked the ships' manifest, they're not sure if we are to load sulphur, or potash. Maybe part cargo of both, so ports of discharge are unknown at present. I do know several people in Australia who may buy the acid. As soon as I find out, we can make better plans. What I do know, and I can tell you is that we will be loading zinc at Port Lincoln for Avonmouth."

"Port Lincoln, as in South Australia?" Stevie asked, his eyes lighting up.

"Yeah! Have you been there before?"

"On the Cape York. We were moving grain to Mombasa from there. I know a couple of people who could maybe buy some, but they only deal in cannabis."

"I know a couple also." Willie said, "I think this voyage is going to go well. Only 3 months. Hey! We'll be back home in no time, and rich!"

'Back home in no time', will be the understatement of the year. It turned out to be 13 months later before I arrived back at home! Fourteen months had past since I was in Port Lincoln? Sandy refused to see me then, would she refuse to see me again? Would she even recognise me? Is she still living there? So many unanswered questions?'

Leaving Seattle, it took 21 hours to reach Vancouver. Another 24 hours to load 14,000 tons of sulphur, and 10,000 tons of potash. Almost 4 week sailing to our first port of discharge; Brisbane, (Queensland), the remaining 10,000 tons were bound for Adelaide (South Australia).

Because I had lost my contact book, I had no way of calling Nora.

After four days of sailing, 9 cylinder heads blew causing a couple of small fires, nothing too serious, but it meant they would be drifting for at least 36 hours, 200 miles east of Hawaii.

So that night Stevie decided to do a bit of fishing. The weather had been good for the past couple of days and the sea was like a pane of glass. Stevie had recently acquired a hardened wire trace. One end was spliced to a customized meat hook, the other to a heaving line which was coiled around one of the poop deck winches. He placed the meat and hook just breaking the water surface, then threw half a bucket of slops into the water. He had come prepared with a half of roast chicken and 6 cans of beer. Stevie pulled up a deck chair sat down and waited, and waited, and waited.

"Needn't have bothered with the clusters lights" He said to himself, looking up to the sky, I could see part of the Milky Way. It was so clear and bright. He had never seen the Moon looking so big! It was a fantastic!

Shortly after midnight, while eating a piece of chicken he noticed a slight movement of the rope, so he looked over the side. The sight amazed him as two white tipped sharks, about 5 to 6ft were actually playing with the bait. Swimming around it in circles, taking turns to approach the bait, the sharks gathered speed just to head-butt the meat, then swimming away in an arc just to have another go. They were taking the piss!

This pattern of play went on for what seemed like hours. Another one had joined the party, slightly larger, maybe 7ft. And Stevie could sense it wanted a lot of the action.

He kept his gaze on the big shark for a further hour or so. It swam away and just as he thought it had gone, he noticed a large dorsal fin rapidly heading his way. "This is it," he thought. He grabbed the rope with both hands, planted his feet squarely against a bollard for support and braced himself. Nothing happened! He peered over the side just as the shark had swam once again under the bait and off in the distance. " Bastard!" Stevie thought as he slackened his grip.

Suddenly, without any warning whatsoever, a huge monster of a shark appeared. Possibly a great white, or a whale shark, the width of its head must have measured at least 4ft. across. It had been lurking below the boat, waiting all this time, just like Stevie was. He, or she, grabbed the bait and was off at full speed.

Stevie was lucky he had released his grip when he did as he would have no skin left on his hands. Fast reactions allowed him to reach the winch, switch it on, and select reverse gear. The rope was so tight, the winch was having problems to haul in. Smoke began to appear as the rope began to burn, yet still, he or she refused to let go. Then suddenly, the rope snapped, the winch started heaving in as the tension subsided. After several minutes the end of the rope appeared, frayed where it had snapped. There was nothing! Absolutely nothing! No trace! No hook! No meat! No shark! No fucking nothing! He or she would always be the one that got away!

The following day, the engineers managed to fix the problems and get them under way. Stevie felt so upset because as they were leaving, he personally counted 17 sharks thrashing around in the water, trying to get aboard.

Because of the inadequacy of the British Ruston Engines, it took almost 4 weeks to reach Brisbane. As soon as the port engine was fixed, the starboard one would break down.

Not one day passed within the 4 weeks that he managed to get more than 3 hours sleep each night. There was very little time for rest, just fix this, or sort that. Just work, work, and more work! What made matters worse was on arriving at Brisbane, they had missed the tides. The port couldn't accommodate them and they had to lay at anchor for a further 3 days. When they finally did moor alongside, a party started.

Davy, Willie and Stevie had decided to take some acid.

"Do you know anyone here who would buy this shit?" Stevie asked Davy. Willie butted in; "There's someone I know in Adelaide, but that's several days away."

"Would you ask them to come here?" Davy said.

"I could, but Adelaide is more than 350 miles away, I doubt they'll travel here."

"What about you Stevie? Anyone?"

"Yeah! In Port Lincoln. Besides, that's 2 weeks away. I've only dealt cannabis with them. I don't have a clue with this stuff."

By now the acid was kicking in. Conversation was becoming slurred and silly. They had planned to go out on the town, but that went out the window. They listened to music, had a couple of beers...

The next thing Stevie recalled was being woken up from a deep sleep by a young couple who had stopped their car as he was lying in the middle of the road in front of them.

At first they thought he was dead, or had been hit by another car. They were shocked to find he was sleeping. He tried to explain but he was having so much problem putting sentences together, they decided to call the police.

The next thing he recalled again was being awakened again, only this time by a huge mountain of a man, who was shouting obscenities at him. Stevie tried to move but his feet were cuffed to a white chair he was sitting on. Also, he could not move his hands as he wore a straight jacket, all in white. In front of him stood a white table on which lay a piece of white paper. That was the only furniture in the room, a white floor, a white ceiling, and yes; white walls.

Two figures entered through a seamless door which became invisible once closed. One was female, the other a giant! The Aboriginal monster's face was inches away from Stevie's, as began stabbing his massive fore finger towards Stevie's eyes shouting; "You're tripping!" Over and over again. When he did not answer immediately, the office would slap him again, knocking the chair over and Stevie landed on his face. He began to freak out, writhing and shaking around uncontrollably.

Stevie thought someone must have taken a pity on him, as all of a sudden the giant left, and the female officer took over. She held a tray containing a syringe filled with a red liquid and placed it on the white table.

She spoke but Stevie could not comprehend. As he tried to speak, he found the words just would not come out. She smiled as she stabbed the back of his neck with the syringe.

The next thing he remembered was trying to have a conversation with a lawyer just before appearing in court in front of a district judge. Whatever the woman had injected in him, it certainly put Stevie to sleep. But it did not help with the memory loss he was experiencing.

"And where did you get the 10 tabs of acid that was found on you?" He kept asking Stevie.

"I don't remember!" He kept telling him.

"If you're found guilty with possession, it carries a ten year sentence. If you say where you got them, the judge would be lenient."

"I told you, I don't remember!" And that was the only words he could muster throughout the entire trial. Stevie got away with custody because he was a foreign seaman and his ship was ready to sail, the judge informed him. He could leave the country, but he had to pay a fine of $5000(Australian). And as the ship was delayed, Stevie had to pay an extra day fine on top of that which totalled a further $2000. As if that was not bad enough, he was dogged 5 days' pay from his salary. A very expensive night out.

Davy and Willie helped him out a lot with the cash they had already earned from their assets. 20,000 tabs had already been sold. They had no idea how Stevie ended up in the street, as far as they knew, when they bid goodbye to him, he was falling asleep in his cabin!

Stevie was lucky not to be sentenced, and became very unsure of 'acid'. Because of his stupidity, he was confined to his cabin and not allowed ashore at the next port. Pity! It was his first visit to Adelaide. He had spent over two years coasting Australia, and this would have been his first chance to visit what he had often heard of, that Adelaide was Australia's most beautiful city. They berthed alongside for 5 days, and all Stevie saw was the sprawling, dirty dock area. Davy and Willie managed to sell more acid. They gave him his share which he did not deserve, but they insisted.

* * *

Once the remaining 8,000 tons of sulphur had been removed, and ballast tanks filled, they set sail for Port Lincoln, a small seaside port in South Australia, a town with a population of around 10,000. A 42 hour sail. "It's been over a year since I was last here." Stevie said to Davy, securing the last mooring rope to an aft winch, they were loading grain.

"Will your contact still be here?" Davy asked lowering the accommodation gangway as they tied up alongside.

"I hope so! But as I've already explained, she deals in 'grass', not sure about acid."

"She?" He sniggered, "I should have known."

"What's that supposed to mean?"

"Nothing! Women will be your downfall Stevie. Mark my words. They're more trouble than they're worth." His trademark loud hearty laugh echoed around the ship. He then got serious. "Can you contact her?"

"She's a Goth and runs her own boutique down town. I don't know where she lives, she never mentioned it to me. I always met her at her shop, or, knowing the schedule of the Cape York, she usually arrived quayside. Tomorrow, I'll visit her shop, it'll be better if I'm alone."

"OK, I'll go with that." He went on, "and you're staying aboard tonight?"

"Yeah. I'm on first watch so I'll be able to go to town in the afternoon. That's the quietest time."

'I began to feel a little apprehensive, and a little scared about contacting her. I dare not tell him she shunned me for 8 months. I had fallen in love with her, my first real love, then after she had her way with me, she ignored me! I tried so hard to contact her, when I realised I couldn't, like all teenage first loves, I began to resent her. I thought she just used me for her own weird satisfaction, then, after she had taken me, she discarded me like a rag doll as though she'd got tired of it. And, to make me feel worse, she refused to see me. Each time I returned to Port Lincoln, there was no sign of her. The deals were negotiated between Graham and I, Sandy was never present. At the tender age of 19, she'd left an impression on me so profound that it would remain with me for the rest of my life.'

At 3pm the following afternoon, Stevie reluctantly entered her boutique. He counted five customers, one at the counter purchasing new outfits, while the others fingered through the huge array of clothing and accessories on offer. He began walking towards the counter when he noticed Sandy emerging from a back room. Although looking slightly older than her 29 years, she still possessed an air of authority and beauty, unmatched in his eyes. She stood 5ft. 8ins tall in her black high heeled boots. Her thick wavy black hair had two purple ringlets running down each of her cheeks from her hair parting, ending at her waist. Behind her, her hair caressed her buttocks as she approached Stevie. Wearing a long PVC dress reaching below her knees, and elbow gloves to match, she certainly had not lost her beauty. She still looked stunning. Searching him with her big grey eyes, she said. "Hello Stevie." Then smiling, "It's been a long time since I last saw you!"

"Whose fault is that? Certainly not mine. I looked for you each time I docked, you knew the schedule of the boat. I don't understand!"

They kissed each other on both checks, followed by a short embrace.

"Can I get you a cuppa? I'll need to speak with my customers just now."

"Please. No milk, nor sugar. Thanks."

She took his hand, and led him into the back room, then went to speak with her customers. When she returned ten minutes later, she placed the cup of hot coffee on a table beside Stevie, lifting her right arm, she suddenly slapped him across his face with all the force she could muster. A sharp stinging pain ran through his face!

"What the fuck Sandy?" Trying to rub the sting away, he felt his face reddened.

"Why didn't you return?" Her nostrils flaring. "Have you any idea the shit I went through when you failed to show. Eric waited two days as Cape York was late. And you weren't on it! I'd invested a lot of money in our arrangement. I lost a heap of customers and nearly the shop." The anger in her eyes was apparent.

Still rubbing his red hot throbbing cheek, Stevie answered her question. "Why didn't I return? Now there's a fucking thing! I DID FUCKING RETURN! 6 FUCKING TIMES! And YOU refused to see ME! I even discovered you're FUCKING MARRIED. Who told me? YOUR FUCKING ASSISTANT!" Without realising, his voice was getting louder. She placed her gloved hand on his mouth, and said calmly, "Drink your coffee, it's getting cold. I have customers to attend"

Stevie was glad she left, as he needed to calm down. He finished his coffee, and as he was about leave, she returned. "I'm really busy just now, how long are you here for?"

"Two days. Maybe three."

"I close at eight tonight, will you meet me?"

"What about your husband? Do you think he'll consent?" Stevie said sarcastically.

"He's a lorry driver, he is often away from home days on end, he left yesterday morning. Not expecting him back for a couple of days." She glanced into the shop. "I have to go!"

Stevie grabbed her arm. "I'm also here cause I've some gear you may be interested in." She broke away from his grasp. "What kind of gear? The same as the last? That was excellent stuff."

"No! I have acid." There was a moment of silence. Then she said, "I've never dealt with that stuff! I wouldn't have a clue how to sell it, and at what price to charge. Look Stevie,

I'll need to go. I'll try my best but can't promise any result. Meet me here at 8."

She then kissed Stevie on his still reddened check. "Sorry 'bout that, I couldn't help myself. Meet me later and I'll tell you MY story." He left puzzled, his cheek still throbbing. "Wouldn't like to tackle her on a dark night." He thought.

"She doesn't know if she can dispose of any of the acid, so, no figures were mentioned, that's the reason for tonight's visit." Stevie told Davy arriving back on board. "Well, we'll need to take some with us, and after your crazy episode in Brisbane…"

"*We?* Only I can meet her." Stevie cut in. "I've already told you that."

"Stevie, I won't be with you, but I'll be there!" With that he left.

Stevie arrived ten minutes early to find the shop in darkness. "Not again!" He thought, but a car horn startled him. He turned round as Sandy pulled up at the kerb. "Get in." As he sat down, Stevie asked. "Where are we going?" "Originally, I wanted to go somewhere quiet so we could talk. But I've managed to get a friend who's interested in the acid."

"We can talk in my cabin if you fancy? Might even buy you dinner, which reminds me, are you hungry?" Instead, Sandy said, "Later! Now, I'll take you back to the ship, and be at this address for ten."

Handing Stevie the address, she said "I'll see you there." Then, dropping him off at the gangway, she sped off.

'Fucking Bitch. Is she playing with me again? She still hasn't answered my questions.'

Arriving at the address Sandy had given him, the three of them entered separately through different doors to what appeared to be a lounge bar. Packed with party goers, dancing to the sound of loud Goth music, Stevie made his way through hoards of Goths, eventually reaching the bar. "A schooner of ale, please." He ordered, handing over a $10 note to the barman. Then looking at the crowd, searching for Sandy, he asked, "That fucking music is piss, and what kind of hair style is that?" when he felt his bum being nipped. "This is not your scene I know." Sandy whispered in his ear. She had changed into a leather outfit and the aroma began filling his nostrils.

"What would you like to drink?" Stevie asked. "I'm not staying Stevie. How many do you have?"

"5000!"

"Tabs?" She sounded surprised. "5000 tabs? Wow, I wished I'd asked back at the shop. So you're looking for around 5 grand?"

"Normally yes, but because I feel I owe you, I'll settle for half that."

"Oh, that's so sweet of you." She kissed him on the cheek. "Wait here, I'll be back." Now he began looking about for Davy. "He must be somewhere there. Surley, he hasn't gone." He thought. Just as he felt a panic attack erupting, Stevie spotted Davy in a far corner. "Glad you're still here." Stevie said sitting next to him. "How many on you?"

"500."

"500?" He was shocked. "I told Sandy I had 5,000!"

"Really?" Davy began looking through his bag. "Okay! Just as well I brought extra eh?" He began laughing "Only winding you up."

"Brilliant! Now I can wind you up! I can only get 5 dollars a tab. Will you accept that?"

"A bit cheap don't you think Stevie?"

He explained that he owed her one, so he had offered it for that price. Davy was not too pleased, but accepted his story and slipped him the package under the table.

"She fucking slapped my face you know!" He laughed.

"You must have deserved it." Stevie was grateful. "Thanks Davy. I owe you one now."

"I know you fucking do, now fuck off!" Returning to the bar there was no sign of Sandy. "Don't panic! She'll be here." Stevie thought to himself, trying to stay calm.

Just then he smelt her perfume. "Hi. I thought you'd deserted me again." She slipped an envelope into his hands. He, in turn, handed her the package which she slipped under her dress top. "Now that's over, can I pick you up at ten? I still haven't told you my story."

"Nor have I told you mine. Ten, at the dock OK?" Sandy said as he followed her out and met up with Davy outside. Stevie handed the envelope over, Davy counted the contents, then they ordered a taxi, and returned back on board. After dinner Stevie showered, shaved, and even managed to shit.

She still looked as sexy after fourteen months. I'd just got all emotions of her out of my head, and now, they are all returning. The chance of her still here, and I happen to return on a one off cargo run. I have to put down as fate.

What else was awaiting him that night made Stevie felt anxious of meeting her. He thought of standing her up as a revenge, but thought that would be selfish. So he decided to go, even if it was just to hear her story, which, he concluded must be good as she would have had fourteen months to perfect it!

Ten o'clock arrived, and right on time she tooted the horn. Before the car door was fully shut behind him, she sped off. Several streets and junctions later, they arrived at a secluded spot where she parked up and switched off the engine. Without saying a word, she reached over and embraced Stevie tightly, kissing his lips for a long time. Her tongue probed deep in his mouth before she broke free. He looked in her eyes. Tears were streaming down her face smudging her perfect make up. After several moments, getting his breath back, he began explaining his story.

"I was ordered off the Cape York in Mombasa. I had no warning, I couldn't let you know. And when I thought about it, you didn't give me your number. You never told me where you lived. You never spoke of your family. In other words; I know nothing about you! I'd known you for only two days, you had your way with me that night, then left a simple note about not making my breakfast. When I returned the following trip, I called into your shop where I got your instructions. My heart broke when your assistant gave me the devastating news that you were married!"

"For that I'm truly sorry. I wanted to see you, but thought better of it due to the circumstances." Tears were forming in her eyes.

"Why Sandy? Why wouldn't you see me? I fell in love with you and you fucked me up." Stevie began sobbing again. After a few sniffles, and intakes of breath, she simply said. "I was pregnant!" It took Stevie several minutes for what she said to sink in. He was lost for words, but he managed to ask; "Boy or girl?"

"A boy! I didn't want you to see me with a bump!" She continued between sniffles. He took both her hands, and looked deep into her big grey eyes.

"But that still doesn't answer my initial question. Did you wanted a last fling before getting married? Was I the first prick you encountered?" They sat in silence for a while. Finally, she spoke. "I want to answer all your questions, and I hope after I've finished you'll understand."

"What's his name?" Stevie asked, not that he was interested but he was just curious.

"Who? My husband or my son?"

"Your husband"

"Graham..."

"No, not THE Graham. Eric and Graham? Whom I had done business with? The big tall one. That same night you fucked me?" He began to feel anger stirring.

Are you gonna listen? Or do I shut up now?"

"Sorry, I'm listening."

She began with Graham, they were school sweethearts. He was the captain of the football team, and she, head cheerleader, so it was natural when leaving school they became a couple. Her father was the local preacher and her mother a laywoman. They both belonged to The Brotherhood; a strict religious sect, she was brought up by their religious rules. Sandy was their only child. "We weren't allowed any luxuries such as television, or radio." She explained drying her eyes. "We didn't possess a fridge nor freezer. I didn't know what it was like to wash in hot water. But worse of all, I couldn't be who I wanted to be. I couldn't dress as I like..." She began sobbing again. Stevie managed to comfort her and once she had composed herself, she continued. "As soon as I left school I was out of the house, and my only option was to move in with Graham. We've been together ever since."

"OK. So where do I fit in to this equation?" Stevie insisted.

"Graham and I have tried for a child. I got pregnant three times." She lowered her head and he could hear her faint sobs. "And three times I had miscarriage."

"I'm so sorry about that. It must have been devastating." He held her, she rested her head on his shoulder.

"It was." She suddenly lifted her head and kissed him deeply on the lips. Then with eyes narrowing, and nostrils flaring, she cried. "You were NOT the first PRICK to come along. This town is full of PRICKS, I could have had anyone I wanted. Remember the first night we met at the bar, I looked straight into your eyes?" he nodded. "I saw your soul, Stevie, and I wanted to touch it. And you know what happened next."

Stevie began sniffing and sobbing. "What are you trying to tell me Sandy? I'm still confused."

"Oh you fool, I'm trying to tell you that MY son is OUR son!"

I just stared at her. Was this another trick women played on men? I was new to all this love shit. MY son?

"You must be mistaken, my sperm isn't old enough to produce babies." Between laughing and crying she smothered him with hugs and kisses. Releasing herself from Stevie she said. "I fell in love with you too, but I knew it could never be. You live on the other side of the world. Once you sailed away, I knew I would never see you again and I didn't want to forget you! That's why, as you politely put it, I raped you. I wanted YOUR child, and that's why I didn't want you to see me pregnant."

"What's his name?" 'This, I was interested in.'

"Graham Stevie Hutchinson. He calls him Graham, I call him Stevie." "Where is he now?"

"Since he was born, my mother has taken a shine to him. She takes him overnight now and again."

Stevie felt his eyes watering again. "And he's five months old?" She nodded, her lovely smile returning to her face and warming the surroundings.

"So what happens now? We kiss and say goodbye? And I'll see you like, NEVER?"

Tears once again filled her large eyes. "We could. Or we could spend this last night together."

"Where should we spend it? My place or yours?"

She began giggling. "Your place."

"And what am I gonna do about this PVC fantasy you've left with me?"

She didn't answer, but started the car and drove back to town. The ship was moored at a different berth from the grain silos as they were loading zinc concentrates. It was a dirtier part of the harbour.

She parked a hundred yards from the ship. Security prevented her going further, so they had to walk the distance. She linked her arm in his and the swish and smell of her outfit along with the clink of her high heeled boots began stirrings in his trousers.

Stevie could hear wolf whistles and calls as they boarded, and was glad to reach his cabin. She stripped immediately and he saw her naked for the first time. Her body was, like he suspected; perfect!

She had a tattooed cobra running up each thigh, their forked tongues caressing her crotch. She had a dragon on her left arm, and Japanese symbols around her tiny waist. Her long silky hair covered them up. She laid on her back, arm stretched out, enticing Stevie to join her. He was naked in seconds and snuggled in beside her. How different it felt from the last time. They made love slowly, deeply, and with so much passion they were lost in each other's lust. She sat on top and rammed her pussy down on him with all her might, her hair bouncing all over, smothering him. She moaned out loudly, shuddering as an almighty orgasm took over her. She made him come three times before he begged her to stop.

"I need some fresh air." Lifting her hair from her forehead, she slowed down, but kept a circular motion on his cock. She began blowing air in his face. "Better? Will I see you again?" She asked increasing her movements.

"I hope so, Sandy. You are my true first love, I will never forget you." With that she kissed him lovingly on the lips, her tongue probing his mouth and whispered "Fuck me, fuck me" over and over again.

Time stood still as if allowing them to indulge in their final lovemaking. Eventually Stevie succumbed to sleep. When he began to rouse, he searched for her, but he was alone.

Not again. Why the fuck is she treating me this way and why the fuck do I keep passing out? Or was it really a dream?

Suddenly he smelled her perfume, then her warm breath was in his ear and her hair falling over his face. "Wakey-wakey my sleepy Scottish Sailor. As promised, your breakfast is ready."

He was suddenly awake. He sat up, both eyes wide open. How she did it, he would never know. She was fully dressed, hair and make-up looked perfect, as if she had never slept. She laid the tray of coffee, toast and omelette beside him on the bed and sat next to him.

"I chatted up that nice cook and he let me help myself." Clasping her hair with one hand so it wouldn't lay on the tray, with her other, she took the fork and cut a piece of omelette. "Open wide, I made this just for you." She placed the egg into his mouth, biting her bottom lip, waiting for his judgement.

"It's lovely." And with that, she kissed him and shoved a fork of omelette into mouth.

"I've been thinking about us and our child and what the future may hold."

"And what conclusion have you come to?" She asked, taking a bite of toast.

"Do you love me, Sandy? Even though I'm almost ten years younger. I know we have wee Stevie, but do you *really* love me? Cause I'm thinking of jumping ship."

She almost choked. Dropping the fork she grabbed Stevie's hands "No, no, Stevie, please you can't. You mustn't. Yes I love you and I don't give a shit about age, but I have a life here I just could not give up. OK, suppose I do come with you. Where would we go? What could we do? You'd be a wanted man. Constantly running from the law." He could see the anger building up in her eyes. "And what happens to me when you get caught? And with a baby in tow?"

She showed Stevie how pathetic, childish and selfish he must have sounded. He felt so immature and downright ashamed. Not only was she beautiful, she was smart, intelligent and perfectly right.

"You're right Sandy, I didn't mean to upset you, I was stupid to think I could stay. Give me a couple of minutes, I'll escort you ashore."

A strange silence fell over them. "I have to tell you something Sandy, I wasn't going to mention this, but I feel I must."

She got up, took the breakfast tray away, placed it on a desk and turning to him, she said. "What do you want to say? I have to go soon, you'll need to get up." With that she tossed his jeans over. "I don't want to leave the ship alone."

"Well, it's not that important, I co..."

"No! Please Stevie, tell me, I may not see you again and that would leave me wondering about it for..."

"Okay, I'll tell you." Stevie hauled himself from the bunk and began explaining how he had met Ann.

"When we were first introduced, for a moment, I thought she was you!"

"Really Stevie?" Her eyes were wide open, with surprise or shock, he couldn't tell.

"Apart from her hair length stopping at her, her eyes green instead of grey, she was my age, well, she was a month older. I found it hard not to think of her as your double. Your identical twin." Turning to Sandy, he said, "Do you think I have a thing for older women?"

"Wow! Don't you think that's weird?" She sat on the bunk and threw him his work denims. "And don't be cheeky. Do you think that's fate? Or destiny, or whatever you want to call it?"

"Only time will tell Sandy. What do you think?"

She held him tight, they kissed for several minutes, he could feel her tears on his lower cheek. Releasing herself from the embrace, she said. "I wish you and Ann all the luck in the world. I truly do Stevie."

Very little was said as Stevie escorted her down the gangway. Closing the car door behind her, and rolling down the window she clasped his hand and asked, "Will I ever see you again Stevie?"

"Maybe Sandy, I truly hope so, just watch out for any drunken Scotsmen in town, you never know, there could be a Baron Boat in town."

Stevie handed her a slip of paper. "That's the company address, I'll get letters if you want to write. I may not be able to answer them, but if you do decide to, please let me know how wee Stevie is getting on. I'd like to know." They kissed each other tenderly again for several moments. Then, slowly driving away, she mouthed *"I love you"*.

Stevie stood and watched her disappear from his life. *"I love you too"*.

'For 18 years I tried to return to Port Lincoln, if not for her then for my son, but that has never happened. In 1981, the worst bush fires in South Australian history engulfed the area for 9 days. It took three of those days for Port Lincoln to be burnt to the ground. To this day, I've heard nothing from either of them.'

* * *

Leaving Port Lincoln, the next port of call was Freemantle (Western Australia) also known as Port of Perth, a sprawling area of industrial warehouses and a frantic bustling metropolis like an overlarge ant nest. Ships of all sizes berthed prow to stern along the never ending jetties and piers. They docked for bunkers, a mere 12 hours, so there was not enough time for Stevie to take in the local sights.

Stevie felt a sense of 'deja vu' from the Cape York. It took him days to clear his head of Sandy. He smoked little and drank even less. The voyage of three weeks across the Southern Indian Ocean was mostly calm. And thankfully, both engines were still running at a speed of 15 knots.

Cheech & Chong reappeared and were still a pleasant sight every morning. But there was still the issue of 25,000 tabs of LSD.

Davy, Willie and Stevie had already earned a tidy amount. They were due to stop again in Cape Town for the usual bunkers, mails and films exchange. They couldn't get rid of any tabs there. The cargo of zinc was bound for Avonmouth, where the present crew would be relieved. They had been on this ship now 7 months. Already 4 months late.

Twelve hours from Cape Town, Stevie was awakened to alarm bells ringing. It was 0525. "What the fuck now." He said to himself, scrambling to get dressed. He noticed also that the boat was rocking and pitching violently, hard to get a firm footing. He bumped into Jerry, the third engineer. He told Stevie 8 cylinder heads had blown on starboard engine and were on fire.

"And the engine room sprinkler systems are fucked!" Jerry informed Stevie.

'All hands below' bellowed out of the speakers, by the time Stevie got there, the entire engine room was engulfed with smoke. "Only those with breathing gear could move down below, the rest will not be needed for now." Said the 2nd Engineer. His face was already black.

Stevie went out on deck and saw plumes of smoke and flames gushing out of the starboard funnel. The seas had now formed a moderate swell, and the ship had to heave to, counteracting the rolling and pitching. Everyone took a turn down below, when one greaser (engine room crew) came up, he would hand the breathing apparatus to the next in line. And so on till Stevie's turn came around. He had a short lesson on its use, then was sent below: It was chaotic. The heat was tremendous. His name was called.

"Relieve Alec over there with the hose." The 2nd Engineer pointed towards huge flames shooting out the engine side. Stevie was surprised he was not offered fire proof clothing. Taking the hose from Alec, he kept it trained on flames emerging from a rip in the engine metal. After what seemed like ages, and as he was beginning to melt, the sprinkler system suddenly burst into life.

He was grateful for the cooling downpour. The 2nd Engineer ordered everyone topside. Stevie scrambled on deck, pulled off the mask and took in several deep breaths. The fresh air felt so good. Looking up, the funnel was still smoking, but he couldn't see any flames. Stevie checked the time; 0815. But it wasn't over yet.

Port side engine had also failed. They were in the hands of the Gods! Through all the chaos, the Captain sent an S.O.S. Seven hours later, two deep sea tugs arrived. Securing lines took some time due to the worsening swell, but once order had been achieved, they began the slow journey to Durban, the nearest port.

At 1500 hours, they moored along side. Work then began on assessing the damage. A portion of the port side structure was removed to allow access into the engine room, and the burnt out cylinder heads were also removed. All the crew members were also assessed. Luckily, no one received any major burns. Apart from smoke inhalation, and scratches, everyone passed a medical.

Stevie was treated for a burn on his right arm and leg. That had occurred when he was caught in a minor explosion. He had to be bandaged in several places and had developed a limp. The Captain then informed the crew that they might be in Durban for a month. As a result, no one was in a hurry to get ashore that night.

Stevie just wanted to catch up on sleep. Davy, Willie and Stevie decided to go ashore after dinner the following evening. None of them had been there before, so they played it by ear.

"Think we'll sell some tabs here?" Asked Willie, as they strolled down a major street. Durban was a large and bustling city in South Africa with a population of 255,000 residence, the size of Sheffield, or Wolverhampton.

"I'm sure we'll find someone." Coaxed Davy. He was always upbeat, that's why Stevie liked him. Davy reminded him, at times of Ricky; with the same 'get-up-and-go attitude'. It didn't take long before they encountered loud music emerging from a doorway. Above the door read 'Your Father's Moustache.' They entered and descended down a staircase leading into a large well lit lounge. Stevie counted at least 3 dozen people mingling about. The room was full of large couches where many sat. Along one wall stood a long and well packed bar where several waitresses ran about trying to keep up with the demand for more drinks. Opposite the bar, a small stage supported a 5-piece rock band blaring out the latest hits. In front of the stage, about another dozen revellers danced away enjoying the sounds.

"There's an empty couch yonder." Pointed Davy. "Follow me!" As soon as we sat, a smiling waitress arrived. "Hi fellows, what can I get ya?" Her long blonde hair tied in a plait, fell below her well stacked bosom. "What do you recommend, we're new here." announced Davy. She gave a slight shiver. Her boobs trembled. "Ohhhh." Her plush red lips formed a sexy pout. "I love the accent. Where are you guys from?"

"Scotland." Said Willie. "Is that where all ya jocks come from? All those Bagpipes. I heard they were made from sheep's guts? Yuk!"

"Haggis is made from sheep's linings." Corrected Davy. She had small but attractive blue eyes with just enough eye liner and shadow to make them appear sexy. She stood about 5ft 7in in her high shiny black shoes. She wore what appeared to be a uniform like all the other waitresses, a red satin outfit. Off the shoulder, flared skirt, the hem reaching just below her crotch, her legs donned in black seamed stockings, seem to go on forever.

"Listen to me rabbiting, you must be thirsty? I'll bring you our best." She turned and left.

Stevie felt stirrings in his groin as it was heavenly watching those gorgeous legs in action. With her short skirt swishing against her round tight buttocks, he almost came. "Wow!" I said, "Have you ever seen legs like that?"

"Are you starting again?" Asked Willie. "Don't you ever stop?" "No! I'm young and learning and want to learn more." Stevie answered, watching with eager eye for her to return. The lounge began to fill up and he needed to find the loo.

"We passed one coming in." Said Willie, turning and pointing towards the entrance. Stevie got up and rapidly headed in that direction. When he returned, their drinks had already been served. No sign of the leggy waitress, nor Davy and Willie. The short time he was away, the crowd seemed to have swelled. The band 'Argent' was blasting out 'Hold Your Head Up, Boy'.

Stevie felt the floor bouncing. He sat down and downed his beer outright. He started to look for 'Leggy', spotted her, and was about to go and chat her up, when Willie and Davy returned.

"Where have you been?" Stevie asked. "Two chicks came over, and asked if we wanted to dance. What would you do?" said Davy.

He was listening, but Stevie's eyes were scouring the crowd. "Who are you looking for, Stevie?"

"No one!"

"Don't lie," said Willie, then to Davy, "He's looking for that waitress."

Stevie then saw her across their table. Getting up and lifting their empty glasses, Stevie asked. "Another? I'll get them." Reaching the bar where she was standing, she broadened her lovely smile as she saw Stevie approaching. "Hi, missed you earlier. You want a refill sweetie?" She took the empties, spun round, as he watched those lovely legs. Following her to the bar, she spun back round saying. "I'll bring them over to your table."

"Thank you, but there's something I need to ask you. What time do you finish?"

"Really? Not until 2am. I get picked up and taken home." She said and his heart sank, but she continued. "But it's my day off tomorrow." His heart quickly rose again. "Could I meet you somewhere for a drink, or a coffee. I find you very attractive." "How long have you been here?" She asked, her lovely warm smile and laughing eyes excited him.

"We arrived last night." Stevie replied. "Do you know Durban?" She asked as he shook his head. "OK, meet me here tomorrow at noon, and we'll have coffee. Now go sit down, and I'll bring your drinks over." She winked and Stevie returned to Davy and Willie. She replenished their glasses all night, and each time blowing Stevie a kiss. They said nothing to each other as by now, the venue was jam-packed, so she was very busy.

As the night wore on, Davy, Willie and Stevie danced the night away. The atmosphere was fantastic. Stevie became a little too drunk and was put into a taxi before the bar closed. Back onboard, alone, and somewhat confused, Stevie was resigned to smoking a joint by himself, and crashing out.

The following morning, slightly hungover, Stevie checked the stores supplies and handed his 'shopping list' to John, the Radio Officer. His work was finished by lunch time which gave him ample time to get ready. He wanted to look his best.

'My confusion from last night continued. Did she give me her name? If so, I was having problems remembering. Do I go and meet her alone? But most troubling is, will she stand me up? Better get going, I don't want to be late!'

She watched him arrive and waved him over. She was drinking coffee. Her age he had guessed last night was about his age. Dressed up as she had, she looked 20-21. Her hair, free from the plait, hung down her breasts in a mass of curls and ringlets. Her sexy blue eyes looked so much larger with heavy black eyeliner surrounding them. Her luscious lips covered in a high-gloss black lipstick, highlighted her sexuality. Her perfume intoxicated him.

Wearing a long yellow polka-dot halter neck dress, she didn't wear a bra. She didn't need to, the straps held her large breasts perfectly. Wearing high black platform boots, he could not glimpse at her fantastic legs. She looked stunning!

"Hello. Sorry I've kept you waiting, have you been here long?" he asked as she gave him a friendly hug. "Only five minutes. You left kinda drunk last night and I didn't get your name."

"Hi! My name is Stevie, was I that drunk last night?" She laughed, teasing him, stretching out her hand she said. "Hi

Stevie, pleased to meet you. My name is Rhoda, and yes, you had a little too much to drink." She giggled. "It was I who put you in a taxi."

"Oh thanks! I don't usually drink that much." She giggled more, Stevie found her laughs to be very addictive.

"So this is your first time visiting my city?" He nodded. "Are you hungry?" He nodded again "Good," She stood up, put a matching shawl around her shoulders, and took his arm saying. "I'm starving too, let's go eat!"

The weather was gorgeous as expected in subtropical South Africa. The streets were busy with shoppers and office workers out for lunch. Stevie felt so proud walking with such a sexy female hanging onto his arm. He wore tight jeans and his bulge became apparent. Feeling slightly uncomfortable, he asked, "Where are you taking me?" She suddenly slowed down, gripping his hand, she led him through an open doorway.

The smell of cooking was overwhelming. His mouth began to water. They found a table and sat down. Looking through a menu she said. "Do you trust me?" He was hesitant, after all, he had just met her. "Sure", was all he could muster. "Then let me order for you. Your first visit to my city, I want you to taste my country. And today, I'm going to show you the sights of my city."

She ordered 'Biltong' for starters, strips of charcoal coloured beef jerky, which didn't look very appetising, but tasted lovely. "Do you like?" She asked stuffing some in her mouth. He grimaced, but ate his portion anyway. "Do you like spicy food?" She asked. "I've ordered 'Chakalaka'" He almost spat out the last piece of beef. "Chakala...What?"

"Chak-a-laka." She giggled. "It's a spicy vegetable curry, one of my favourite dishes. I hope you like it!" It tasted very good, rich and smooth, with a fairly hot spicy taste. Stevie's tongue and lips were tingling. She talked a lot about her hobbies, her friends, her family. She just loved to talk, stopping occasionally to ask questions about his life. At one point he thought she was on speed!

She was a lovely woman, happy and carefree, Stevie was enjoying her company. She insisted they go 'Dutch', which he agreed, and minutes later, leaving the restaurant, she took his hand, and they walked down towards the beach front. The weather was so hot, with the curry he had just eaten, sweat was beginning to run down his forehead.

"Here," She stopped and produced a hankie from her purse, "The sweat is running down your face." she began drying his forehead. The streets were full of sightseers, and shoppers. They dodged skateboarders, and half naked roller skaters. "Where are we going?" Stevie asked, nearly tripping over a dog lead. "To the beach."

"I sign on at 6 pm Rhoda, I won't have time." She looked disappointed. "Oh, I didn't realise Stevie."

Stevie explained to her how he managed to ended up in Durban. "We're here for engine repairs, and that's substantial, it could take up to 6 weeks for repairs."

"Really?" Her face lit up.

"Sorry, I should have told you, I assumed we were only having lunch."

Looking at her watch, she said. "We still have an hour or two, so let's go and get some ice cream."

She flagged down a 'Zulu Rickshaw', a highly colourful horse and carriage, and instructed the driver to take them to 'The Golden Mile'. A bustling promenade lined with high-rise hotels, entertainment complexes, shops, and restaurants. The broad, warm golden sandy beaches was a magnet for water sports enthusiasts, surfing, swimming, fishing, or just basking in the glorious sunshine. Lifeguards and shark nets protected the beaches all year long.

Rhoda told the rickshaw driver to stop along the broad beach avenue where they entered the first of many ice-cream parlours along the front. After that, she led Stevie down a busy ocean-front path, jostling with more skateboarders, cyclists, pedestrians and joggers.

"Where are we going Rhoda".

"Mini Town."

"What's that? A pub? Remember Rhoda, I'm working tonight"

"You'll see!"

Mini Town was a full miniature layout of Durban including The Golden Mile, Victoria street market, Ushaka Marine World, and the airport. All in fantastic detail.

"What day is this?" Stevie felt embarrassed asking.

Giggling, she replied. "Wednesday, why?"

"I'm off duty Friday night, I'd like to see you again."

"I'd love to, but I'm working that night. There's a famous South African band playing on Friday evening, they're named 'AC. Excitement'. Have you heard of them?"

"No!"

Her eyes lit up. "It's a sell-out, but if you ask for me, I can get you in. Do you fancy coming?"

"OK, I'll be there at 10. Who do I ask for Rhoda? I don't know your surname!"

"My surname is Evra, but if you just ask for Rhoda, I'll get the word."

"Thanks for a lovely day Rhoda, I like your city, I'll see you on Friday."

They hugged and kissed each other good bye. The taxi she ordered dropped Stevie off at the jetty.

'She was attractive, sexy, with a bubbly personality, she was a lot of fun to be with. More importantly, she was the third woman I'd met since I joined the Merchant Navy who wasn't a whore!'

The ship repairs took almost two months. Some of the parts had to be flown over from the UK. Rhoda and Stevie saw each other three times each week. She was always dressed immaculately, and very sexy! She showed him as much of her city as possible within the time they were together, and he had a continuous hard on. She introduced Stevie to her friends and family. Then, on the last night in Durban, they made love. She made him cum so many times, his cock was red raw.

"Rhoda, please my love, I can't take any more." As she once more tried to stiffen his feeble cock.

"I've been wanting to fuck you since day one." She proceeded to lick and caress his balls and arsehole. "I noticed your discomfort on our first date. I've been so horny since."

'Why, when I meet someone I could spend some time with, someone not a whore, someone gorgeous and sexy, I have to say goodbye. Am I doomed to know only hookers? If Rhoda had asked, I would have jumped ship for her. Our parting was very emotional. She stood quayside waving till she became a dot in the distance. I will never forget her.'

The ship was an utter mess with all the engine work that had been carried out on her. Her superstructure and accommodation facilities were thick with oil and grease where dock workers discarded everything without thought. All hands were employed to clean up and make the ship look respectable, and shipshape for the voyage home. Once that was achieved, the tedious task began to give her another lick of paint from bow to stern.

Two weeks had gone past, and, as they re-entered the Northern Hemisphere, the Captain ordered all hands on the poop deck for a meeting.

"I understand when you join this ship it was scheduled for three months," The Captain began, "and as you all know, we are now four months behind schedule. Because of that fact, the contract has lapsed. We are heading for Gibraltar to await orders. The chief steward and I are in the process of arranging crew reliefs for those who wish to go home. One thing I'm thankful for, the engines haven't let us down this far. Are there any questions?" "What about the cargo, Sir?"

"Very good question, Davy, but I can't give you an answer. We are 5 days from Gibraltar. Hopefully I'll receive orders before then. If not, we'll drop anchor and wait. Are there any more questions?"

They all looked at each other, then back to the Captain shaking their heads.

"OK then, all those wanting to be relieved, give your name to the Chief Steward. Otherwise carry on men. Dismiss!"

All those hoping to go home from Gibraltar were disappointed to hear the following day that they had received orders to discharge full cargo in Kokkola, Finland.

* * *

Eight days later, they sailed through the English Channel. Many of the crew showed their disappointment of being so close, yet so far away from home.

Normally, that wouldn't bother me, but this time, nearing home, I began to think of Ann. I'd received many letters from her in each port where mail was distributed. Then, after months of unscheduled delays, I received a letter from her telling me she was pregnant. It devastated me! Memories of Sandy and Graham came over me, I put myself in Graham's shoes, he was bringing up my son. I thought of Ann bringing up her child alone. I will need to play it by ear when I meet her again.'

The journey through the North Sea, he was thankful for as they encountered good weather. Then into the Oresund Straights, Copenhagen starboard, Malmo on the port side, and under the Oresundsbron Bridge, which brought them to the Baltic Sea. The weather change took effect on Stevie. From months being in hot weather conditions and wearing very little, to feeling fucking freezing! They sailed along the Gulf of Bothnia heading towards Kokkola, positioned to the far north of the gulf. They were almost in the Arctic circle. Stevie was thankful that it was late summer, it felt relatively mild, but still fucking freezing!

Tying up was difficult as the jetty was shorter than the ship, her bow and stern jutted out at each end. There were only two large fixed shoreside cranes available to unload two hatches, so two of the ship's cranes had to be employed.

A snow storm had passed over the port the day before, therefore there was an accumulation of three feet remained everywhere. That night, Davy, Willie, Matt and Stevie headed for the nearest pub. In an effort to keep warm, Stevie wore his coldest weather gear, but it was still inadequate as he did not pack for the cold. In fact no one did. The town was very picturesque, especially as it was covered with snow. They slid and staggered their way towards music blaring from the only colourful building around, and entered a large lounge bar. There were about a half dozen locals drinking, or eating. A large stage stood at one end supporting a 4 piece band who was struggling with the sound effects and trying hard to entertain diners. After a couple of 'Skols', they decided to return back on board.

Davy invited all three of them to his cabin for a night cap where he produced the remaining 'acid' tabs. "2,500 of those" He said, throwing several sheets of blotting paper on his desk. "And about one and a half grand in cash."

"I can't get rid of any tabs" Stevie said.

"Neither can I" Said Matt.

"What about you Willie?"

"I'm not sure Davy, why? What have you got in mind?"

"I can get rid of all of them and if I do that, I'd split the cash between you three. So that's £500 each, we have a deal?" The three of them looked at each other, and without words, nodded. They all shook hand, exchanged money and said goodnight.

As they left the cabin, Willie turned to Stevie and said. "Fancy meeting up in Glasgow next week for a pint or something?"

"Sure. Where?"

They exchanged phone numbers and arranged a call to each other.

Another storm arrived early the next morning, breaking two of the three bow moorings. All havoc broke loose. Large breakers laid only yards from the jetty. The ship would have beached on them causing severe damage, and impossible to free. A tug arrived while Stevie was frantically getting dressed. The three emergency services were also present. All the deck crew were up at the bow trying desperately to secure the only fixed mooring which was threatening to give way. Finally, after several hours, the ship was back alongside, and well secured.

The following two days went by with no more hiccups. The ship was finally unladen, and she was ready for her final voyage with these dodgy engines. She set off from Kokkola on a three day sail to Antwerp, where she was due to change her jinxed engines. And the crew finally relieved.

Was I glad to get off this ship? In a way, yes! She was fraught with problems, but I learned many things on her. I discovered I had a son. Foolishly, I had a run in with the Australian law and luckily, I got off lightly. If the police had raided the ship, I would be in jail! Instead of a "Very Good" stamp in my discharge book, for the first time I would have received a "Good" stamp. Only one word difference, but I would have problems trying to join my next ship.

After being home at his mum's for two days, Stevie bought a train ticket for Glasgow. He had contacted Ann and arranged to meet her in a room at The George Hotel in Buchanan Street. After they made love almost everywhere in the room, Ann began to confess.

"I never planned to get pregnant, Stevie, it just happened. The result of a one night stand."

Stevie tried to put himself in Graham's shoes and wondered if Sandy had uttered similar words to him. Without thinking any more, he took Ann's hands in his, and simply asked; "Will you marry me?"

Looking deep into Stevie's eyes through her tears, she simply said; "Yes!"

Two weeks later, at the register office, they were announced man and wife! Willie was his best man, and a lassie named Harriot was thrilled to be the best bridesmaid.

Epilogue

Thrown into the deep end so young, Stevie had no real adolescence experience, he had to grow up very quickly. Each time at home when on leave, he would spend some of it with old school mates, but after a short time, he realised how immature they were. In their companies, he soon grew bored with their childish behaviours. He had accepted the fact that he was, and would always be, a loner!

His family knew nothing of his smuggling, why would they? His grandfather, mum's dad, owned a coach building factory, employing over two thousand people in its heyday, building war planes during the Second World War. After the war ended, it became a major coach builders and a car repair garage, complete with its own panel beaters, paint shop, repairing cars of all sizes, even HGVs. If they had known that the 'Black Sheep' of the family was smuggling drugs throughout the globe, it would bring total shame on them. Stevie therefore had learned to keep his mouth shut. He kept himself to himself.

Entitled to two days leave for every month away from home, he found that he had accumulated several weeks leave after the long voyages involved. After two weeks at home, Stevie and Ann decided to move into a Glasgow council flat. It didn't take long before he became restless, and soon discussions were focused on him returning to sea as Stevie wanted to return to work.

He telephoned head office to ask for any vacancies even though Ann was not pleased about him returning to the boats, especially with the long voyages involved. So he managed to talk head office into giving him shorter voyages. He was told of Cape Howe, a 33,500 tonnes 'ore wagon' as they were looking for a second steward.

"How long are the trips?" Stevie asked Peter.

"Between 6 and 8 weeks" he was informed. "Normally to Murmansk in Russia, or Port Cartier in Nova Scotia."

"I'll take it." Stevie was enthusiastic, he couldn't wait to tell Ann. He explained to her he would need to leave the following day for Middlesbrough.

Stevie was only 19 when he married Ann, he thought he was in love. He was willing to take on Amanda, and bring her up as his own daughter. In those days, single mums were scorned upon, so he gave Ann an engagement ring and within two weeks, they were man and wife. It was a turbulent marriage, they split up after 3 years, but reconciled 18 months later, after bumping into each other at a party. Nikki was conceived, and born 9 months later.

Stevie arrived home early one day to find Ann in bed with a stranger. After an almighty row, she destroyed his seaman's books, which ended his seafaring dreams and making it impossible for him to return to sea. His smuggling career was forced to come to an abrupt end.

Or so he thought!

Stevie decided to take the PSV (Public Service Vehicle) driving test. When he passed, he got a job driving buses for Glasgow Corporation, where he met Alec Cassidy, his conductor. They formed such a good relationship, workmates christened them 'Dutch Cassidy and the Sundance Kid'. They hit it off immediately, becoming best buddies. Alec was three inches taller than Stevie, standing 5ft. 9ins. barefoot. He had contracted polio as a child which left him with a distinctive limp. His fair shoulder length hair was always kept immaculate, along with a moustache, well chiselled jaw, large lips, and deep blue eyes, made him attractive to women. He also had the gift of the gab, always quick with one liners, and usually cheered up any dull party!

When he married Isabel, Stevie was his best man. Stevie and Alec parted for several years as Alec brought up his family whilst Stevie moved to Hamilton, working for Central Scottish Omnibuses.

Seven years later, Alec appeared back in Stevie's life, asking if he wanted to go into business with him operating ice-cream vans. Their run was in Ardrossan. This was the first time Stevie had heard that name in many years. He never dreamt that one day he would be living there! He remembered the first time ever when he saw the name written across the stern of one of the Baron Boats, he had thought it was somewhere in India! He even had problems trying to pronounce it. He thought he was joining a foreign vessel. He never realised it was in Scotland!

Ardrossan was also where Stevie first met Libby. They got on well together although Stevie wouldn't call it love. They spent many fun nights together, their love making was very passionate. They had lived together for only 9 months when, after getting drunk on Alec's birthday, he was persuaded to sell the ice-cream van and accompany him to America.

To his surprise, when he returned from America, Libby was waiting for him as he had sold the van and taken off with Alec without much discussion with her. Plus, he certainly had not treated their relationship seriously. Despite that, they rekindled their relationship and moved to Stranraer to stay with Libby's aunt.

A year later, Alec appeared again, inviting Stevie to join him and his family in Spain. He had just bought a bar in Benalmedena, on the Costa-del-Sol and was keen to show Stevie around.

The visit turned out to be a disaster! In 1989, Spain was hit by the worst floods in Spanish recorded history. Alec lost everything in the flood.

In that same year, Stevie re-ignited his smuggling days, moving three and a half tons of cannabis into the Canary Islands. But alas, he was arrested on Hogmanay that year, and spent 9 months on remand in Tenerife.

Returning to the UK, Libby was, once again, waiting for him. Love and affection for her were beginning to grow inside Stevie. Feeling grateful, he began to wonder if she really was his soul mate. They continued to live in Stranraer but Stevie could not find a job. Just then, out of the blue, Alec arrived with yet another offer of a job...

(But that's another story!)...

Printed in Great Britain
by Amazon